THE
HISTORIC TÂF VALLEYS
Volume Two
In the Brecon Beacons National Park

Cover Illustrations

From an original water colour painting by the well-known Dowlais artist Thomas Prytherch (1864-1926). It shows Pentwyn Reservoir (Dolygaer Lake) and part of the valley before the impounding of the water for Tâf Fechan reservoir. On the extreme left of the picture near to the overflow was the Pentwyn Inn (not shown) and on the extreme right Dolygaer Railway Station. The building in the foreground is the Vicarage and behind is Dolygaer Farm surrounded by trees.

Frontispiece (overleaf)
Detail from The Ordnance Survey 1" map of Breconshire, 1832.

THE
HISTORIC TÂF VALLEYS

Volume Two

In the Brecon Beacons National Park

GEOLOGY
SOCIAL HISTORY
NATURAL HISTORY

1982
Merthyr Tydfil and District Naturalists' Society

DESIGNED AND PRINTED IN WALES BY
D. Brown & Sons Ltd., Bridgend, Mid Glamorgan

Contents

CONTENTS

Foreword

from the President of the Society,
DOUGLAS W. THOMAS, F.R.C.S.

Following the successful publication of the *Historic Taff Valley PART I* (Quakers Yard to Aberfan) the Merthyr Tydfil & District Naturalists' Society now present *PART II*. This covers the area of the upper reaches of the Tâf Fechan and Tâf Fawr from their origins in the Brecon Beacons to the confluence south of Cefn-Coed-y-Cymmer. The Society has been fortunate in retaining the services of such able contributors as Dr. Mary Gillham and Mr. John Perkins to write on their subjects of Natural History and Geology respectively, while Mr. Jack Evans − who has an unrivalled knowledge of this area − has contributed a fascinating and generously illustrated section on its history from neolithic times to the present day. The Natural History and Geology has been cleverly designed to coincide with a series of walks which take in most of the major tributaries. One such walk − Beacons Reservoir to Llwyn-On − is absolutely new and is fully described here for the first time.

For lovers of the countryside and in particular those who cherish the Beacons, this volume will provide many exciting hours of exploration and discovery.

Acknowledgements

The Merthyr Tydfil and District Naturalists' Society is very grateful to the Merthyr Tydfil Borough Council for the interest they have always shown in the activities and publications of the Society, and for their financial help which is so readily given.

Financial support has also been generously granted by the Vaynor Community Council, the Michael Sobell Charitable Association, the Welsh Water Authority and Mid Glamorgan County Council.

We are greatly indebted to the following for supplying photographic illustrations: Mr. Keri Williams, Mr. Richard Evans, Mr. Glyn Davies, Mr John Yates, Mr. John Wright and Mr. Jim Lloyd. Mr. Mansel Jones supplied pen and ink sketches.

Of inestimable help in proof reading were members of the editorial committee: Messrs Frank Baguley, Douglas Thomas, Bob Evans, Clive Thomas and Jack Evans.

Finally we would like to thank all those people, too numerous to name, who, in one way or another, have helped in the production of this volume.

Introduction

by DAVID BRYNMOR THOMAS, M.B., B.S., B.Sc., B.Sc.(Lond.),
D.Sc.(Birm.), F.R.C.Path., F.I.Biol., F.R.S.(Edin.).

*Bute Professor, Head of the Department of Anatomy and Experimental Pathology
and Master of The United College of St Salvator and St Leonard
in the University of St Andrews.*

The Tâf Fawr and Tâf Fechan descend from the Brecon Beacons and converge to become confluent at the *cymmer* that distinguishes Cefn-Coed-y-Cymmer from the many other wooded ridges which adorn—or which formerly adorned—the Welsh landscape. Both rivers are guided to their confluence by valleys which I would consider to be interesting and significant as well as beautiful even if I had not had the good fortune to grow up in the community which they accommodate. This book is about these valleys and their inhabitants.

The beauty of the two valleys will be evident to the most casual car-bound visitors but their more interesting and significant features will be appreciated only by those who escape from their cars and reject the constraints imposed by the roads. Even a limited amount of active exploration will reward them with an insight into the relationship between the beauty and variety of the scenery and geological features, with an opportunity to observe the rich flora and perhaps with a glimpse of the inconspicuous fauna. This book will provide them with invaluable information.

It will also help those who wish to consider the distinctive features of an environment that has exerted its influence upon the community which it has accommodated since the hostile climate of the last ice age started to improve.

This environment is crossed by the boundary between the old red sandstone to the north and the carboniferous limestone to the south, by the boundary between Powys and Glamorgan and by the boundary between rural Mid-Wales and industrial South Wales. For centuries it was too far from Brecon and too far from Cardiff to be readily subjected to administrative control from either centre and the ruins of Morlais Castle are an attractive monument to the failure of de Clare and others to establish their authority here. At the same time it was too far from Llandaff and St Davids to be readily influenced by the hierachy of either diocese.

The characteristics of the environment are reflected in the religion, philosophy and politics of the cohesive and vigorous community which it has nurtured—a community which maintains continuity with the past without failing to respond to the demands of the present or to anticipate the uncertainties of the future.

Part One: Geology

JOHN PERKINS

Introduction

Half a kilometre south of Storey Arms a well-beaten pathway leads eastwards from the A470. In a few metres it crosses the young Tâf Fawr and climbs steadily up the hillside towards Corn Dû and Pen y Fan. This well-worn popular route to the highest mountain in South Wales, for Pen y Fan reaches 880 metres, follows the crest of the Brecon Beacons. Northwards, there are views down steep slopes towards the darker green of wood and farmland along the Usk Valley, and to Brecon, on the River Usk itself. To the south, much longer gentle slopes drop gradually towards the distant rim of the South Wales coalfield.

Just before the path reaches Corn Dû it levels out, on a narrow ridge separating the slopes of the Tâf Fawr valley from those of its neighbour to the east, the Tâf Fechan. The summit of Corn Dû, a few hundred metres beyond, is really the northern end of this dividing ridge or watershed between the two rivers.

The walker who looks south from the top of Corn Dû has a view of both valleys, and can readily notice their similarities – the sloping, grass-covered upland ridges, here and there marked by hags of wasting peat; below, the dark conifer plantations and the gleam of water in the reservoirs with which each has been endowed by man.

Below, to the west, the A470 is perpetually busy with traffic, cars streaming over the pass at Storey Arms, bound to and from Brecon or, perhaps, the Brecon Beacons Mountain Centre near Libanus.

The footpath to the east is well-worn, and the commando-soled boots of its innumerable walkers have removed all trace of plant life from it, as they head for Pen y Fan. For some, a drive along the road; for others a visit to the Mountain Centre; for still others again, a walk along this ridge-top pathway; these are some of the meccas, the tourist honeypots of the Brecon Beacons.

From this upland vantage point, the differences of detail, the variety of natural forms, of Geology, of Natural History and man-made history, individual to the Tâf Fawr or the Tâf Fechan, these all remain hidden. Nor can the eventual junction of the two rivers, 14kms (10 miles) away at Cefn Coed just north of Merthyr Tydfil, be seen.

What a place the summits of the Beacons are, to visit in the different seasons of the year, to walk up the track on a mist-covered Autumn day,

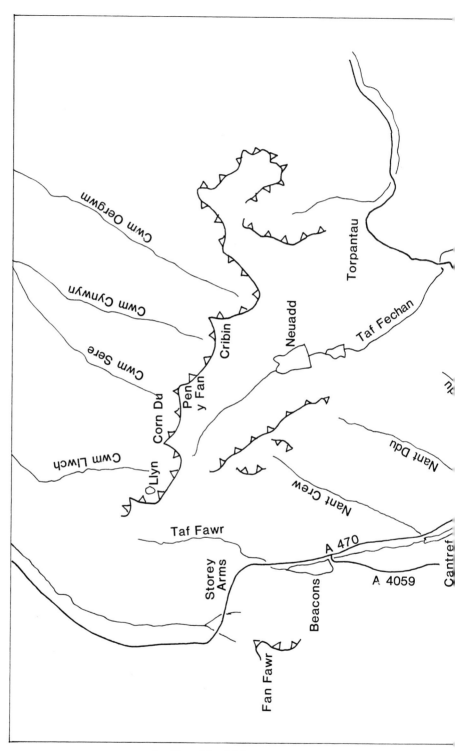

1   Map of the Area.

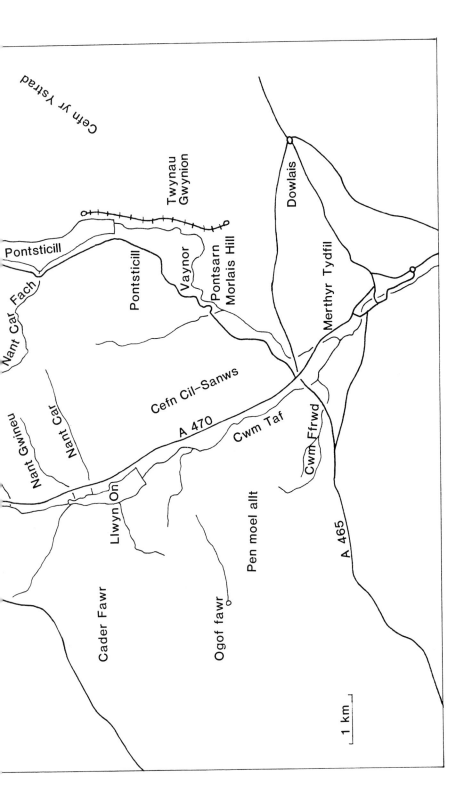

1 km

13

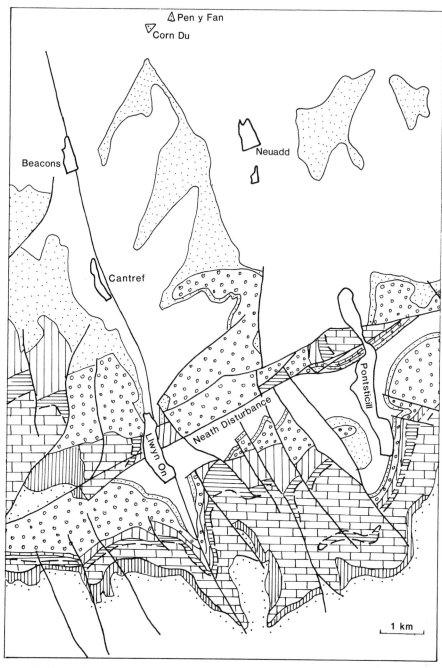

2 Sketch Map of the Geology of the Area (based on the maps of the Institute of Geological Sciences, with the permission of the Director)

KEY TO GEOLOGICAL ITINERARY MAPS — Figures 11, 22, 24, 28, 33, 37, 39 and 46

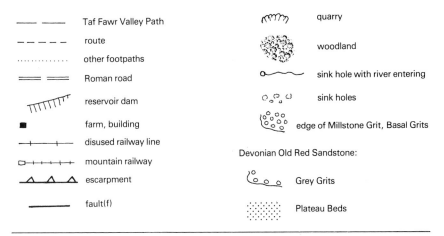

—— ——	Taf Fawr Valley Path		quarry
– – – –	route		woodland
············	other footpaths		
=== ===	Roman road		sink hole with river entering
TTTTTT	reservoir dam		sink holes
▪	farm, building		edge of Millstone Grit, Basal Grits
—+—+—	disused railway line		
□+++++	mountain railway	Devonian Old Red Sandstone:	
△ △ △	escarpment		Grey Grits
——	fault(f)		Plateau Beds

when the hiker is cocooned in a silence broken only by the honking of a raven sailing effortlessly overhead through the oblivion! Or, to come up near dawn on a cloudless Summer morning of limitless sky and distant horizons. In Winter, snow returns the summits to their glacial appearance, icicles marking the seepages along the marly beds of the northern scarp faces, the slopes ribbed in black and white bands as snow lies on the shale beds but leaves the vertical edge of each sandstone standing out as a dark line.

It is this grand, imposing northern scarp of the Beacons which provides the Mountain Centre with its superb panoramic view of the hills. The steep slopes, all in the Old Red Sandstones, soon drop down to the Usk Valley and the northern boundary of the park, but however, much of the variety and interest of the Brecon Beacons lies on the southerly or dip slope.

It is about that country, the land between the twin sources of the Tâf and Merthyr Tydfil, that we write — not just of the frequently visited parts, the areas served by main roads or well-known footpaths, but of the less walked, less explored backcountry — the lovely tributary valleys, the hidden remains

KEY TO GEOLOGY SKETCH MAP

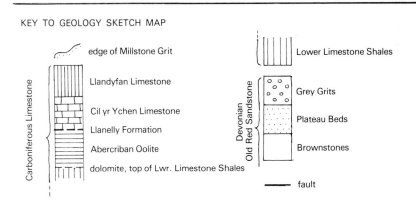

Carboniferous Limestone			Devonian Old Red Sandstone	
	edge of Millstone Grit		Lower Limestone Shales	
	Llandyfan Limestone		Grey Grits	
	Cil yr Ychen Limestone		Plateau Beds	
	Llanelly Formation		Brownstones	
	Abercriban Oolite			
	dolomite, top of Lwr. Limestone Shales		fault	

of man's activity in quarries and tramroads, the secret worlds of wildlife, on moorland, in the forests or in the reservoirs.

For the northward traveller the Brecon Beacons begin when he leaves Merthyr Tydfil, not when he reaches Storey Arms. The upper Tâf valleys are an integral and fascinating part of the park's southern districts and too many visitors pass through them without realising their potential interest. Admittedly, by-roads are few, but, for the explorer willing to walk a little there are rich rewards.

One of the more easily gained rewards is to take the circular drive through the mountains, say from Merthyr Tydfil via Pontsticill up the Tâf Fechan, then over the pass at Torpantau into the Talybont Valley. Continuing west then to Brecon, the traveller can return over the main road route to Storey Arms and so back to Merthyr. Who would deny that this is a most satisfying day out, scenically and aesthetically – at least five major reservoirs are passed on the way. Their contribution to what could well be called the lake district of South Wales is in no doubt.

This book first describes the landscape, its origin and structure, then going on to study the natural and man-made history of the area. The study includes the Tâf Fawr and the Tâf Fechan valleys down to their junction at Merthyr Tydfil and a new long distance path down the main valley, providing a direct link between the coalfield and the crest of the Beacons, is identified. Each section also describes a number of walks into the backcountry where features of special interest may be seen.

Throughout, the reader should refer to the 1:50,000 Geological Map (Solid and Drift editions), Sheet 231 Merthyr Tydfil, and for localities and place names to the 1:25,000 Ordnance Survey Map, Brecon Beacons National Park, Central Area. Contours on the latter are still given in feet but its scale, not quite 2½ inches to the mile, relates easily to the metricated Geological map. We have tended to use both systems of measurement here and ask the reader to bear with us since this book is appearing at a time when both systems are in use, and some confusion remains anyway! Remember that the national grid squares on both 1:25,000, 1:50,000 and old one-inch maps have sides 1km long anyway, so it is easy to work out approximate map distances.

Finally, do not underestimate these mountains. Many people have done so and paid dearly for forgetting that poor weather, poor equipment and other factors can make even a Welsh mountainside of less than 900 metres in elevation a very dangerous place.

The Geological Succession

				Rock unit	Description	Thickness
PLEIST-OCENE	RECENT			Peat, alluvium, gravels		
				Glacial sand and gravel Boulder Clay		
.... unconformity						
CARBONIFEROUS	Namurian	West-phalian		Coal Measures above Farewell Rock	Sandstones, shales, thin coals	
		Millstone Grit		*Gastrioceras subcrenatum* marine band	Shales	
				Shale Group	Shales, mudstones, thin coals, goniatite bands	46-61m
				Basal Grits	Quartzite and conglomerate	37m
.... unconformity						
	Dinantian	Carboniferous Limestone		Llandyfan Limestone	Light grey oolite Honeycomb Sandstone Light grey oolite	12m
				Cil yr Ychen Limestone	Dark, blue-grey limestones and oolites	107m
.... unconformity						
				Llanelly Formation	Calcite-mudstone	9m
.... unconformity						
				Abercriban Oolite	Oolites, dolomites and calcite-mudstones	24m
				Lower Limestone Shales	Dark grey shale and thin limestones, dolomites	21m
DEVONIAN	Breconian / Farlovian	Old Red Sandstone	Upper	Grey Grits	Grey-green quartzitic sandstones	
				Plateau Beds	Red sandstones; quartz conglomerate at base	30-76m
			Lower	Brownstones	Red and brown sandstones, grits and marls	396m
				Senni Beds below		

Confusion has developed over the years in the nomenclature of the Carboniferous Limestone succession as attempts have been made to revise and refine it. In this account the names used are those which are given by the Institute of Geological Sciences on the new (1979) 1:50,000 Solid Geological map, Sheet 231, Merthyr Tydfil. Based on rock character, these names closely relate to the original fossil zone classification by Vaughan, which is also referred to occasionally in this text. Previous revisions of his fossil zones, whose initial letters were derived from the fossil names, were later thrown into confusion because all the zone fossils but one have since been re-named! In an attempt to sort matters out the Geological Society of London has proposed yet another scheme, ie, a third classification. The history of the problem is set out in the tables which follow:

Vaughan's Zones	Vaughan revised	New fossil names given since
D Dibunophyllum (Coral)	D_3 (= Upper Limestone Shales) D_2 D_1	
S Seminula (Brachiopod)	S_2 S_1	renamed Composita (C!)
C Caninia (Coral)	C_2 C_1	renamed Syphonophyllum (S!)
Z Zaphrentis (Coral)	Z	renamed Hapsiphyllum (H!)
K Cleistopora (Coral) (K was used to avoid two C zones by Vaughan)	K	renamed Vaughania (V!)

On this basis we should not have Vaughan's K, Z, C, S, D zones then, but a sequence of V, H, S, C, D! The confusion caused by the renaming is obvious. In addition, as described later, the upper Tâf valleys lie close to the northern limit of the Carboniferous Limestone outcrops so there is a thinner sequence. Parts of the succession are missing locally for this reason. Further gaps are also present, due to local uplift, erosion and removal of some of the beds shortly after their deposition. So, in this district only the K, Z, S^1, S^2, D^1 and D^2 beds are represented. These can be related to the 1979 Geological Survey names and the new Geological Society of London stages in a second table:

Succession of Carboniferous Limestone

Geological Survey	Vaughan	Geological Society of London	
		Formation	Stage
Llandyfan Limestone	D_1	Penderyn Oolite	Asbian
Cil yr Ychen Limestone	S_2	Dowlais Limestone	Holkerian
. . . . unconformity			
Llanelly Formation	S_1	Llanelly Formation	Chadian
. . . . unconformity			
Abercriban Oolite	Z	Gilwern Oolite Clydach Beds	
		Blaen Onneu Oolite Pwll y Cwm Oolite	Courceyan
Lower Limestone Shales	K	Lower Limestone Shales (Courceyan also includes the uppermost Old Red Sandstones)	

The Origin of the Rocks and Scenery

The key to the geology of the upper Tâf valleys is a simple one, a series of layered or bedded rocks tilted towards the S.SE. The layers are built of sandstones, mudstones, grits, shales and limestones, all of them formed as sediments. The series of layers is not complete for many geological events have occurred since the rocks were formed and erosion has removed the upper layers, especially from the central and northern areas of the Beacons, Figure 3.

The rocks all belong to two of the major periods of geological time, the Devonian and the Carboniferous. Studies of these rocks have enabled geologists to make detailed reconstructions of the geography of South Wales in those far away times. It is a story which illustrates the drifting of the continents, for in Devonian times much of Europe (and hence South Wales and the Brecon Beacons) lay south of the Equator in what are the southern desert latitudes.

Figure 4 shows a bird's eye view of the area at that time. Mountainous tracts occupied St George's Land as geologists have named it (mid and north Wales). From its hilly districts, periodic flash floods washed down red muds, sands and grits, to build out river flood-plains. These bordered a coastline which lay approximately where the Bristol Channel is now.

Europe was drifting northward towards the Equator; indeed it has crossed and continued to drift northwards ever since, to bring it to its present latitude. Approaching the equatorial regions, the semi-arid flood plains of Devonian times were gradually submerged beneath warm tropical seas, marking the beginning of the Carboniferous period, Figure 5. A sequence of carbonate sediments was laid down. Thus the Carboniferous Limestone of South Wales forms a wedge-shaped group of beds, thickest near what was

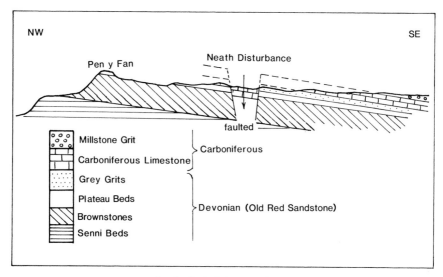

3 Geological Cross-section.

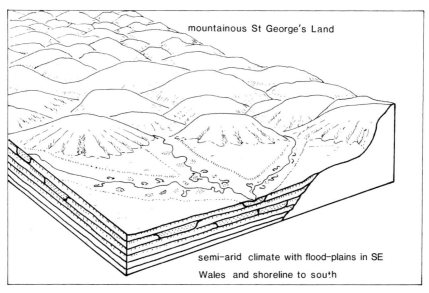

4 South East Wales in Devonian times.

the deeper water to the south, and thinning northwards onto the old landmass of St George's Land. The thin northern edge of the wedge has been eroded away in our modern landscape but there is enough left of the thinner sequence in the North Crop of the Coalfield/southern Brecon Beacons to allow a glimpse of the conditions at the time of formation.

The seas extended northwards onto the old semi-arid lands, but the submergence was not a progressive, uninterrupted action. For two periods the seas retreated again and so the general northward advance actually took place in three stages – all recognised within the bottom part of the Carboniferous Limestone succession, the Lower Limestone Shales.

Today, Carboniferous shales and sandstones laid down in the deeper water to the south are exposed in the rocks of Mid-Devon. If we could go back to Mid-Devon in Carboniferous times and make an imaginary journey northwards to St George's Land (Wales), as the sea became progressively more shallow we would first notice an increase in sandy material, and mixed with this fragments of shelly fossil debris.

Further north the sea was shallow enough for shoals, and the movement of waves and surface currents agitated debris on its bed, rolling fragments of sand and shell about until they became coated with limy material, forming ooliths. Ooliths give oolitic limestones their fish roe appearance.

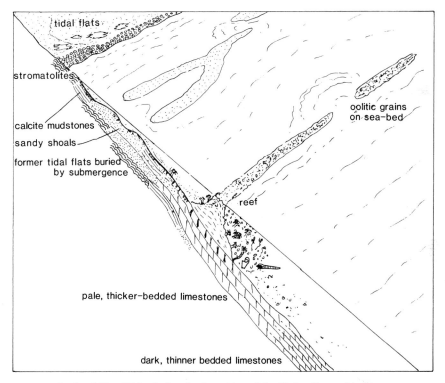

5   South East Wales during the deposition of the Carboniferous Limestone.

Beyond the shoals, sand-bars, lagoons and tidal flats were formed, with mats of algae trapping limy grains within their structure. Here, tidal effects and periods of drying out associated with temporary recessions of the sea would be most noticeable.

Reaching St George's Land, we would notice a flattish coastal landscape, alluvial with soil cover and primitive plant forms.

Since the encroachment of the sea onto the land was gradual, so the various zones noted on this imaginary journey would each have migrated slowly northwards, depositing their distinctive sediments over those of their predecessors. The intervals of recession which occurred were marked by drying out, by the exposure on land of the zones nearest the shore, and so erosional surfaces with development of limestone solution features and karst layers occurred. The next re-advance of the sea, crossing over such areas, would then rework the deposits and produce an unconformity in the rock succession.

These kinds of fluctuation, evidence of the transgression and recession of the sea in Lower Limestone Shale time, were produced by changes in the level of the land and sea areas, by slight movements of subsidence or elevation. However, near the shore and on the land areas, similar variations could be brought about by climatic change, eg, humid conditions giving way to semi-arid ones for perhaps several thousand years. Such changes can be observed higher up in the Carboniferous Limestone succession.

After the overall northward advance during the deposition of the Lower Limestone Shales, the main oolitic part of the sequence was laid down in less changeable sea conditions. But, a period of shallowing and drying out, marking a change to a semi-arid climate was to follow, producing that part of the succession where old karst surfaces, ancient soil horizons and other indicators of a temporary return to land conditions and an erosional setting can be found – in the Llanelly Formation (see Baltic Quarry, page 65).

Later, renewed subsidence brought the sea back into the area, again with good limestone forming conditions. However, the land areas to the north still existed, and rivers flowing in from them gradually poured sediments in

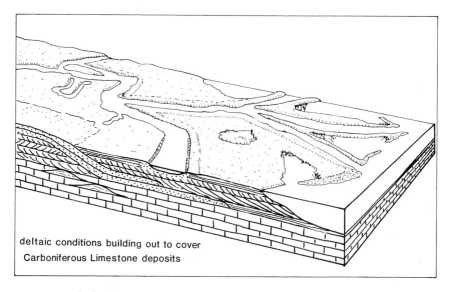

deltaic conditions building out to cover
Carboniferous Limestone deposits

6   South East Wales during the deposition of the Millstone Grit beds.

to the warm shallow waters, forming deltas of muds, sands and, occasionally, of more pebbly conglomerates. These sediments are the beds of the "Millstone Grit," which is obviously more varied than its popular name implies.

Note the great difference in appearance of these new flood plain and delta deposits from those of the Devonian Old Red Sandstone. The former are red in colour, due to the semi-arid climatic conditions of the time, but the Millstone Grit deposits though formed under similar physical conditions are brownish in colour, the products of a humid climatic regime.

Changes in land and sea level were also characteristic of the deposition of the Millstone Grit (and of the succeeding Coal Measures, although these are only represented now to the south of the area included in this study). Periodically subsidence allowed the sea to flood back over the swamps and deltas and lay down marine muds, distinguished in the rock record by their marine fossils, named after their characteristic goniatites and known as marine bands.

Of the rest of Carboniferous time, of the muddy swamps supporting the coal-forming forests, the upper Tâf has no record left. However, the South Wales coalfield lies only a short distance to the south and the rocks preserved in it were once present over the upper Tâf area. They have since been eroded away, Figure 7.

Missing rocks are always a problem to the geologist — were they once there and have since been eroded away? Or were they never deposited in that particular area? What is the meaning of a gap in the overall rock record? It is something like a detective trail that suddenly grows cold, there are no more

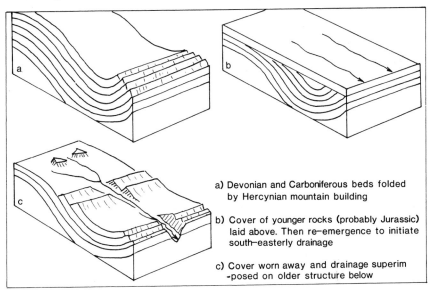

a) Devonian and Carboniferous beds folded by Hercynian mountain building

b) Cover of younger rocks (probably Jurassic) laid above. Then re-emergence to initiate south-easterly drainage

c) Cover worn away and drainage superim -posed on older structure below

7   Folding of the region, deposition of a younger rock cover, its removal and the superimposition of the southeasterly drainage.

clues, no actual rock record to interpret and the missing pages of earth history must be inferred from other information, usually from events known elsewhere.

There is an enormous gap in the local record following the Carboniferous. What is certain is that at the close of the Carboniferous period a mountain building event, the Hercynian orogeny, affected the rocks of South Wales (and of many other parts of Britain and Europe) and that this gave the layers of the upper Tâf their south-southeasterly tilt. Thus, the Brecon Beacons are an escarpment, their steep northern face being formed by the ends of the tilted layers, while the long southerly slopes where the Tâf Fawr and the Tâf Fechan flow, form their upper surface.

Figure 7 relates the evolution of the upper Tâf landscape, taking the story into the long aeons of time since the mountain building and tilting occurred. There is no rock preserved locally to tell us about the events in that long interval from the end of the Carboniferous period 280 million years ago up to the events of the Ice Age, about a million years ago.

In the intervening 279 million years the Permo-Triassic, Jurassic, Cretaceous and Tertiary periods of geological time came and went, leaving rock records in other areas. At some stage in this long interval some of these younger rocks may have covered South Wales but, if so, all trace of them has been worn away again.

Geologists believe that the South Wales river pattern, the strikingly parallel courses of the two Tâfs and their neighbours, is due to their originating on a S.SE sloping cover of younger rocks which has since been removed. The Jurassic or Cretaceous periods may have supplied this cover, nowadays the former being more favoured as the one responsible. As the cover was worn away, so the local rivers were lowered onto the buried tilted layers of older rocks below and began their task of carving out the landscape we see today.

The rivers went about their process during the Tertiary period, and then they were temporarily interrupted in the task by the most recent event to affect the region, the Ice Age. About a million years ago glaciers took over, adding the most recent rock evidence to the story, the glacial clays and sands which are plastered intermittently over the hillsides and valley bottoms.

Reference to Figure 7 shows how the long period of erosion, by rivers, by ice and again by rivers, has produced the present landscape. The Coal Measures and the Carboniferous Limestone have been stripped back, to re-expose the Old Red Sandstone at the surface over much of the upper Tâf valleys.

Some of the Old Red Sandstone beds are more easily eroded than others and the details of the present landscape are due to their varying responses. As the river systems have developed so has the importance of the tributary valleys, and in the upper Tâf districts good examples of both strike and dip valleys may be seen. The main rivers, flowing in the same general direction as the dip of the rocks, are dip streams. Their tributaries, often at right angles

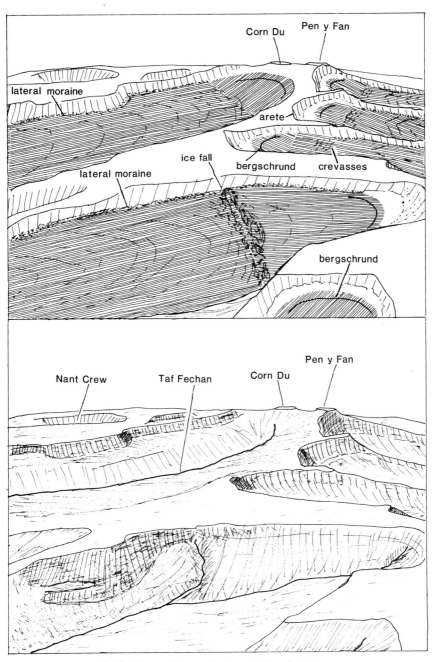

8 The Brecon Beacons during and after glaciation.

to the main rivers, follow the eroding edges of the rock layers, slipping sideways as the latter are removed. Thus, at right angles to the direction of the dip, they are strike valleys, Figure 9.

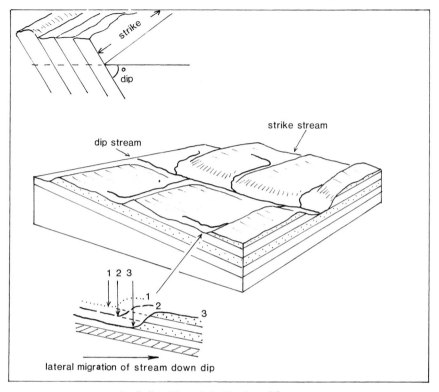

dip stream

strike stream

strike

dip

1 2 3

1
2
3

lateral migration of stream down dip

9   Strike, Dip and the Erosion of Outcrops.

The New Tâf Fawr Long-Distance Path

From Storey Arms follow the west side of the A470 southwards, meeting the Tâf at the old Pont ar Dâf (987196). The old bridge lies east of the road below the recently constructed embankment. Continue south between the road and the uppermost reservoir, the Beacons Reservoir, and below the dam take the A4059 right for Hirwaun. At 988181 just beyond the bend in the road, take the trackway into the forest on the left. If desired, a short diversion up the A4059 to 987177 provides views of several small waterfalls in the Nant yr Eira as it tumbles over the thicker beds in the Old Red Sandstones.

The forest track follows the old railway line used to bring stone up for the construction of the Beacons Reservoir (see Section Two). At the south end of the wood it emerges onto open hillside where its level has been disturbed by small stream erosion and hillside soil movements, visible evidence of alterations to the local slopes in the last 85 years, since the railway was in use.

The track enters forestry plantations again in 0.75km, and 0.25km further on, the trees hide an old quarry on the slopes below, near the head of the Cantref Reservoir. Leave the forestry track and work down through the

26

woodland towards the reservoir bank at 994155 and continue along to the dam. Note the granite coping to the rims of the weir, which is otherwise

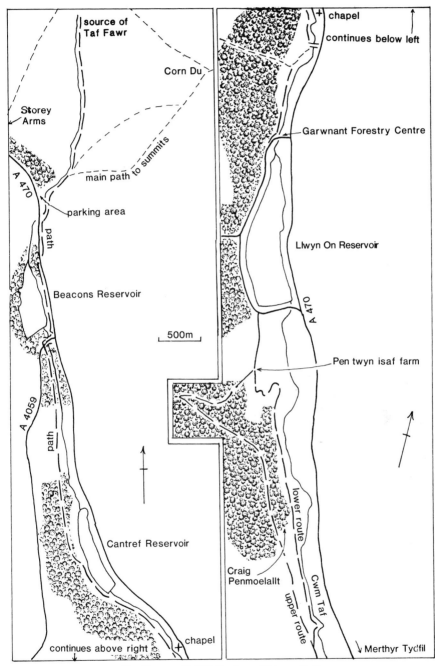

10 The new Taff Valley Long Distance Path.

constructed of Carboniferous Limestone. The greater strength of granite was necessary for the areas likely to suffer the most wear.

For 0.5km beyond, the path follows down to the river bank opposite the small chapel near Berth-lŵyd, 004147. A strong wall had to be built to protect the chapel and its burial ground from being undermined by the Tâf. From this point, the next 0.75km of the route awaits more precise identification, for it enters fields at present under lease to a local farmer. A footbridge provides access to the east bank and the A470 at 005143, 0.5km south of the chapel, and the road can be followed down to the turning west for Cwm Cadlan and the Garwnant Forestry Centre, thus rejoining the river near the head of Llwyn On Reservoir.

However, a legal right of way runs SW from the footbridge across part of the leased land, passing the remains of several long deserted farms, each one perched on a remnant of one of the many small river terraces which are a feature of this part of the valley and which kept them safely above flash flood level. From 003139 on this right of way, follow a field boundary south to reach the road to Garwnant Forestry Centre at 004132.

The road can then be followed all the way along the west side of Llwyn On Reservoir, giving fine views of the slopes east of the lake and particularly of the glacially oversteepened sections where the Nant Gwineu and the Nant Car plunge steeply to pass beneath the A470 and enter the reservoir. The car park/picnic site at the southern end of the reservoir is also the start of one of the walks to be described later, to the Nant Sychbant and Ogof Fawr, and the main valley path follows the first part of that walk, turning up the lane southwards from the Llwyn-On dam and climbing steeply towards Pen-twyn-isaf Farm.

Pass through the farm yard and across the field beyond, to the gate which takes the track into the woodland. Reference to the map, Figure 10, shows that two routes are now available. The upper one follows the track up into the forest, to 003101, where it diverges from the Nant Sychbant walk, page 47, and doubles back to the impressive forested scarp of Graig Penmailard, noted for its whitebeam trees.

Craig Penmailard is a corruption of Pen moel allt; the spelling shown on the O.S. 1:25,000 map is therefore incorrect.

This upper route then continues S.SE down the sloping surface of the rocks responsible for the craig, in winter giving an impressive view of the similar but barren Darren Fach above the A470 opposite, and rejoining the lower route at 079207, just north of the Heads of the Valleys road.

The lower route turns off left through the woodland immediately after entering the gateway and then performs an S-shaped curve down past an old barn to reach a track running S.SE along the foot of Craig Penmailard. Geologically this is the more interesting route, since, as the Tâf approaches Merthyr Tydfil it passes into the Carboniferous Limestone and Millstone Grit beds, and several interesting features can be seen (see Cwm Tâf walk, below).

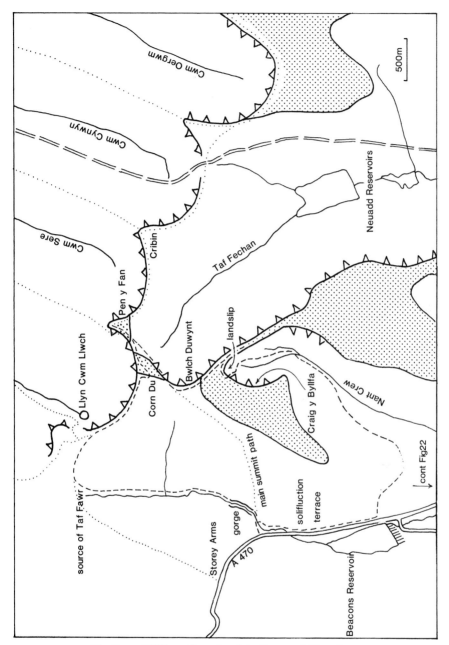

11   Upper Tâf Fawr, Summits of the Beacons & Nant Crew.

From either route, beyond 079027 pass under the Heads of the Valleys road and so into Merthyr Tydfil. The Brecon Beacons National Park Authority, in cooperation with the landowners, ie, the Forestry Commission and the Welsh Water Authority, intends to define the route described above as a long distance pathway, so providing walkers with a direct route from the Beacons to the coalfield.

The Upper Tâf Fawr and the Summits of the Beacons

This walk begins 0.5km south of Storey Arms, at the end of the lay-by left from a remnant of the old road by the re-alignment of the A470. Take the path eastwards from the end of the wood, through the kissing gate and over the stepping stones to the far bank of the Tâf, the start of the main route up to Pen y Fan.

Notice the fine solifluction terrace to the south, formed by successive deposits of soil and stones working down the long slopes under freeze-thaw conditions, Figure 12. Nearby, the Tâf has trimmed away the edge of the unconsolidated terrace material. The terrace continues south of Pont ar Dâf, bordering the A470 until well beyond its junction with the A4059.

After crossing the river, turn left up the main track, but, well before the obelisk which marks the acquisition of the Brecon Beacons by the National Trust with the help of the Eagle Star Insurance Company in 1969, turn left again to keep close to the river. A narrow track follows the eastern bank and shortly leads into a narrow gorge. The walls reveal alternating shales and sandstones of the Old Red Sandstone (Brownstones) and cross-bedding can be seen in the western wall.

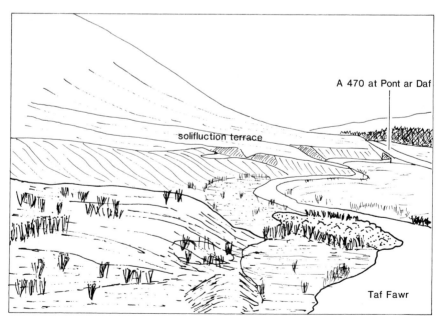

12   Solifluction terrace in the upper Tâf Fawr.

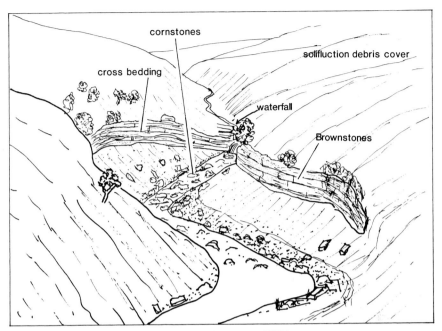

13   The gorge of the upper Tâf Fawr.

The blocks in the river bed are red and green in colour, typical Old Red Sandstone material, but some when broken open reveal angular fragments of grey limestone. These are cornstones, evidence of fossil soil formation in the semi-arid conditions of Devonian times. Elsewhere in South Wales such impure limestone beds are known as "race".

Near the top of the gorge the V-shaped outcrop of the lower unit of a thick sandstone forms a waterfall, but its upper layers have been worn back upstream where they create small sections of rapids. Follow the track up the slopes to the right, to gain the bevel edge between the cut made by the river and the long slopes leading eastwards up to Corn Dû. Follow the edge northward for about 0.5km.

From this vantage point the walker can appreciate how the upper reaches of the Tâf Fawr lie between this long solifluction slope and Y Gyrn, the Old Red Sandstone ridge to the west. In postglacial times the stream seems to have slipped sideways down the long slope to rest against the rock ridge opposite, Figure 14. Now the reason for the gorge can be seen. In being pushed against its western flank, the Tâf has not followed the exact line of its pre-glacial route and has cut the rocky gorge across a spur that was originally part of its western valleyside.

The walker can now continue up the river to its source at 992220 and there join a footpath coming up from Storey Arms to curve round onto the flank of Craig Cwm-llwch, near another obelisk. This one was erected in memory of little Tommy Jones, a child found dead here.

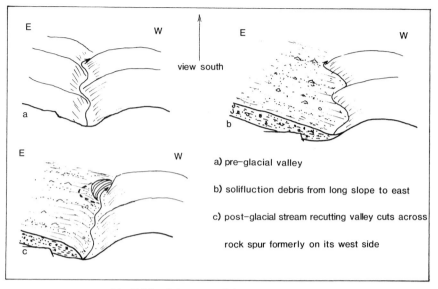

a) pre-glacial valley

b) solifluction debris from long slope to east

c) post-glacial stream recutting valley cuts across

rock spur formerly on its west side

14   Origin of the gorge of the upper Tâf Fawr.

Cwm-llwch is a fine example of the series of once glaciated valleys which are cutting back into the main scarp face of the Brecon Beacons. Because they have the advantage of a lower base-level in the River Usk to the north, these valleys, Cwm-llwch and its neighbours to the east, Cwm Sere, Cwm Cynwyn, Cwm Oergwm and Cwm Cwareli, are steepening up their valley heads, increasing the fine scarp-faces of Corn Dû, Pen y Fan and Cribin and enlarging their valleys at the expense of both the Tâf Fawr and the Tâf Fechan, Figure 15. Indeed, the drainage around the crest of the Brecon Beacons is often cited as an example of potential river-capture.

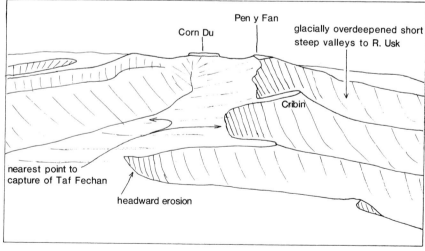

15   The potential river-capture of the Tâf Fechan.

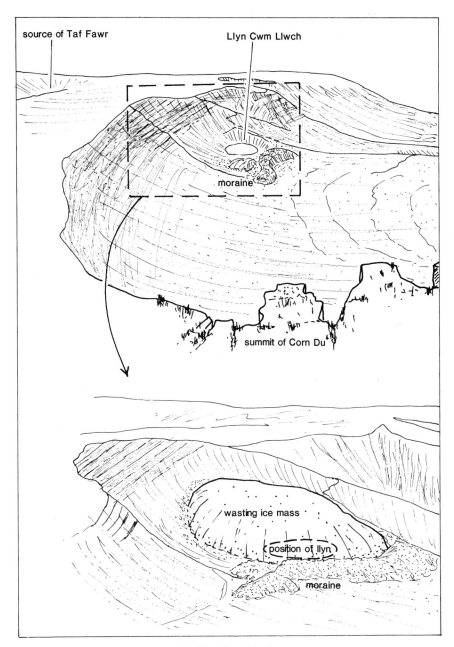

source of Taf Fawr

Llyn Cwm Llwch

moraine

summit of Corn Du

wasting ice mass

position of llyn

moraine

16   Llyn Cwm Llwch.

From the Craig a fine "aerial" view of Llyn Cwm-llwch can be obtained. Notice how the tiny lake is located below the southwest wall of the valley head, in the very spot where the last remaining blocks of ice would have survived at the end of the Ice Age. As these blocks melted and shed the rock fragments they contained, so a ring of debris built up around them, thus forming the circular moraine which now encloses the lake. Thus Llyn Cwm-llwch originated in similar fashion to what geologists call a kettle-hole. Continue up onto the summit of Corn Dû and rejoin the main pathway along the scarp crest.

The direct route up to this spot, the main path up from the National Trust obelisk, by-passes the interesting gorge and the nearer views of Llyn Cwm-llwch and has little of geological interest to offer, except a study of the damage and erosion caused by thousands of walkers' feet. The dip of the rocks is across the path to the right, S.SE, and as the path is widened on that side, so the joints allow portions of the beds to erode away, overturning onto the pathway. Seen out of position, they can give a false impression of the true direction of dip of the rock layers.

From Corn Dû traverse across to Pen y Fan, to observe more details of the northerly scarp-face of the Beacons and of the headwater area of the Tâf Fechan to the south.

Although strictly speaking outside the boundaries of the present study, the north-facing scarps of Corn Dû, Pen y Fan and Cribin are too instructive to ignore. They display sections through important units of the Old Red Sandstones which play major roles in the scenery of the Tâf valleys to the south. The scarp faces also illustrate superb examples of soil creep and mass wasting, typical of many of the steeper hillsides throughout the area.

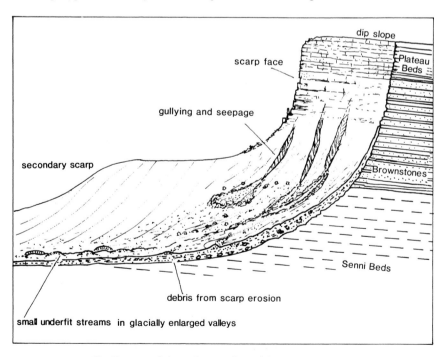

17 Features of the main scarp face of the Brecon Beacons.

The triangular-shaped upper areas of both Corn Dû and Pen y Fan are formed by the Plateau Beds, a resistant group of red sandstones near the top of the Old Red Sandstone sequence. Between the two summits the Plateau Beds have been eroded away and the scarp crest is in the underlying Brownstones. So the ridge is a fine example of differential erosion, lower in the less resistant Brownstones, its peaks still protected by cappings of the more resistant Plateau Beds. In contrast, the narrow ridge to the south at Rhiw yr Ysgyfarnog, 014196 to 010200 and to be seen later on this walk, still preserves a very thin remnant of the Plateau Beds and illustrates the last stage before the isolation of another summit area, around Craig y Byllfa.

A view down over the scarp-face of Corn Dû or Pen y Fan shows how both units of the Old Red Sandstones exposed here, the Plateau Beds and the Brownstones, are composed of alternating beds of well-jointed red micaceous sandstones and softer red marls. The difference between the two units is due to their different proportions of each type of bed, while the alternation of sandstone and marl is the key to the erosion of the scarp-face.

Groundwater percolating down through the rocks is fed out into the scarp-face along all the less permeable marly layers. It is a characteristic of the Old Red Sandstone, a good run-off of water even at quite high landscape levels, and it is surprising how well these rocks store water. Even in dry summers the high level seepages are active.

Emergence of water along all the marly layers leads to erosion, and eventually under-mines blocks of the sandstone beds immediately above. Loosened away along their well-developed joints, the blocks then fall down the scarp-face.

The process is equally effective at all seasons, for in winter the expansion of water on freezing within the marls, and in the joints within the sandstones, can also dislodge blocks from the face. The unstable nature of the scarp-faces is amply illustrated for those who venture along the track a few feet below the north face of Corn Dû, or along the lower one which traverses the north face of Cribin.

Debris from all this erosion gradually accumulates in the scarp-face valleys to the north, and from the summits, streams such as Cwm Sere and Cwm Oergwm are seen to be meandering amidst the accumulations of loose soil and boulders. Far from appearing as vigorous mountain streams, they have the look of mature rivers wandering about on gravelly flood-plains. Clearly this is a landscape which is being worn away by mass wasting and solifluction and the task of the river is to cut the central line, and remove the material presented to it by these slope erosion processes.

Some of the best examples of slope erosion occur immediately below the NE face of Pen y Fan, Figure 18. Tangled, interwoven debris fans lace the bottom of the scarp-face with fine examples of stony levees marking the edges of the individual supply channels.

Before leaving the summit area of the Brecon Beacons, notice the well-developed secondary escarpment on the ridges to the north. Dropping

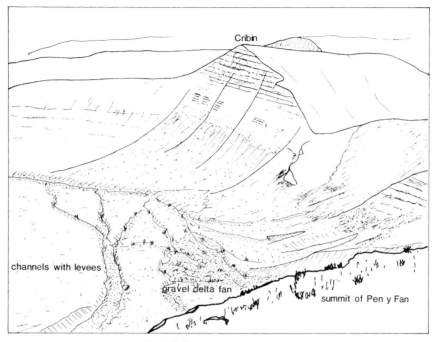

Cribin

channels with levees

gravel delta fan

summit of Pen y Fan

18   Debris Fans below Pen y Fan.

steeply from the main scarp all the ridges flatten out between 540 and 600 metres. The steeper slopes below the secondary scarp are cut in the beds beneath the Brownstones, in the underlying Senni Beds.

Views to the east and south reveal the more conical form of Cribin, which now lacks a preserving cap of Plateau Beds, and beyond that the scarp is breached by a col leading through from Cwm Cynwyn to the Tâf Fechan. The old Roman road crossed the Beacons here and can be seen ascending the eastern slope of the Tâf Fechan towards the col. The col is the nearest point for a breach into the Tâf Fechan drainage to occur and Cwm Cynwyn the stream most likely to achieve a future river-capture, Figure 15.

Beyond the Tâf Fechan, the flat summits of Gwaun Cerrig-llwydion and Craig y Fan are capped by remnants of the Plateau Beds. Down valley to the S.SE, the Neuadd and Pontsticill reservoirs of the Tâf Fechan can be seen, and on clear days a distant view of the Pennant Sandstone scarp and other hills of the coalfield, 15km to the south.

From Pen y Fan return SW and take the "by-pass" path along the southeast slopes of Corn Dû to the ridge at Bwlch Duwynt, 005209, where the main path comes up onto the Tâf watershed from Storey Arms. Bwlch Duwynt has lost its protective capping of Plateau Beds. Small exposed "pavements" of Brownstones a short distance to the south reveal closely-spaced joint patterns and give the surface of the sandstones such a regular appearance that they seem like a man-made paving. This spot makes a convenient break in this itinerary and those who wish to divide it into two walks can return down the main path to Storey Arms.

Nant Crew

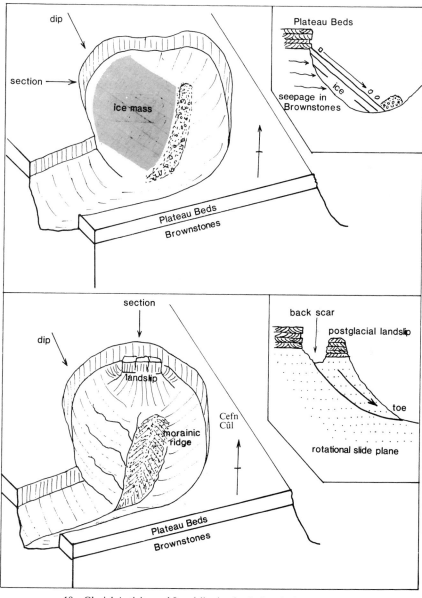

19   Glacial Activity and Landslipping in the head of Nant Crew.

From Bwlch Duwynt follow the watershed between the two Tâfs southwards. The ridge soon rises gently onto another protective remnant of the Plateau Beds, quite an extensive one which continues along the ridge top for 5km, before it in turn is capped by the Grey Grits (the topmost unit of the Old Red Sandstones), and also extends SW in lobes which cover the ridges around the Nant Crew, Nant Ddu and Nant Llysiog.

The Nant Crew has come nearest to breaching this cover and eroding back into the catchment of the Tâf Fechan. Only a narrow strip of Plateau Beds survives on Cefn Cûl, and its active destruction is amply illustrated by the many frost-heaved and loosened blocks which are cambering over and gliding away on either side. The ridge can be examined before turning towards the Nant Crew.

It is best to try to reach the Nant Crew valley at the point immediately north of its source, 007203. This can be awkward when coming direct from Bwlch Duwynt in low cloud or misty weather. It may be best then to reach the Cefn Cûl ridge first and then back-track around the head of the valley.

Groups not wishing to descend into the Nant Crew can continue round the valley head to Craig y Byllfa and then downhill to reach the A470 near the Beacons Reservoir dam, but some fine features will be missed by doing this.

At 007203 there is a fine example of a small landslip, Figure 19; a detached mass of Plateau Beds has begun moving down into the Nant Crew valley, leaving a well-developed landslip chasm to the rear. The whole headwater area of the Nant Crew, as far down as the marked bend in direction, is filled with debris, its valley floor a large remnant patch of boulder clay. The upper limit of these glacial deposits forms a ridge around the east slope of the

20   The Nant Crew Landslip.

valley, about half way up, probably the remnants of a lateral moraine, and the walk descends from the landslip onto this feature and along it down to the bend in the river.

While traversing the valley notice how the main slope erosion and mass-wasting is from the northern and western sides where the dip of the rocks, and hence the flow of groundwater, is towards the Nant Crew. The south and east valleyside, as you look down towards the bend, with rocks dipping into the hill, is relatively more stable. Ground-water flow within the rocks, coming down dip from the north, emerges into the Nant Crew or the Tâf Fechan before reaching the Cefn Cûl ridge, Figure 19. The ridge thus marks a low point in the local water table and illustrates how once a ridge has become as narrow as this, its final destruction may be greatly slowed down.

Keep on top of the old lateral moraine until it forms a spur feature close to the bend. It is easy to descend the point of the spur then and cross the stream.

Following the north bank down for about 0.5km, two interesting small waterfalls can be seen, Figure 21, their detailed arrangement depending on the angle at which the stream course intersects the joint pattern in the Old Red Sandstones.

From the second waterfall, continue along the northern valleyside, following the 525 metre contour level (approximately!) to the spur between the Nant Crew and the Tâf Fawr. From the spur there is an excellent "aerial" view of the Beacons Reservoir and its dam.

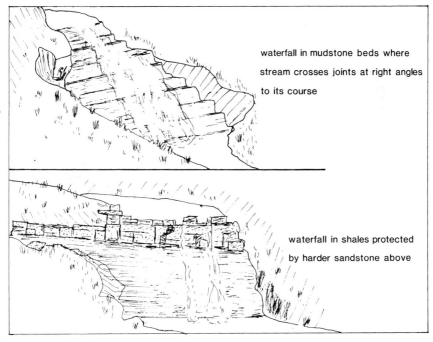

waterfall in mudstone beds where stream crosses joints at right angles to its course

waterfall in shales protected by harder sandstone above

21   Waterfalls in the Nant Crew.

This is the southern end of the slopes which created the fine solifluction terrace seen at the beginning of this walk, and the still active danger of movement here is illustrated by the snow-break fences erected below, close to the A470. Descend to the stile which crosses the bottom fence near the reservoir dam and return along the roadside to Pont ar Dâf and the starting point of the walk. It traffic permits, cross to the west side of the road to examine the blocks constructed along the river bank below Pont ar Dâf. They are not a full-scale embankment, but a measure to keep the river flow on channel and to reduce bank erosion along that stretch.

Nant Wern Ddu and Nant Llysiog

Park at Pont Llysiog, 006141, a bridge on the old A470, now left as an access road to fields to the east. Entrance to the old bridge is only from the southern end, ie, it is not a true lay-by, nor an obvious one, and care is needed in getting into it, for the re-aligned A470 road at this spot is a fast section.

Take the track N.NE across a leased field to the edge of the forestry plantation. After passing through the gate by the ruins of an old farm, keep right towards the stream and follow the lower edge of the wood. Eventually a deeply cut part of the stream is reached with small waterfalls, pot-holed bed and exposures of the Old Red Sandstone Brownstones. Remnants of an old sheep-dip can be found, constructed in one of the stream's deeper clefts. The highest waterfall is a fine example of control by a thick sandstone bed, capping the less resistant layers beneath.

The falls section is due to the adjustment of its course by the Nant Wern Ddu following the overdeepening of the main Tâf valley during glaciation.

Up-valley near the end of the woodland, constructions designed to slow down flash floods can be seen. These were erected in the 1950's. Firstly, on the north bank is a large stone-faced embankment, designed to make flood waters swing and then slow down. From the bend just above note the fine torrent tract down which previous floods have crashed and roared.

Why is the Nant Wern Ddu so prone to them, say in comparison to the Nant Crew? Examination of the map and the dip of the rocks provides the answer. The stream is a strike valley, cutting its course along the rock outcrops at right angles to their direction of dip, page 26. Thus it has more tributaries on its north bank where the dip is towards it, feeding water out of an extensive interfluve area, than it does on its south side where the dip is away from the stream. Now, examining the topographical map, note the extensive interfluves above. The valley is surrounded by a plateau surface, part of the outcrop of the so correctly-named Plateau Beds. In relation to the valley size, the Nant Wern Ddu/Nant Llysiog system has a very extensive upland gathering ground around its headwaters. The whole of its run-off is concentrated into this one local valley when downpours occur. Such a system is a sure candidate for flash floods. On a larger scale, the River Lyn system

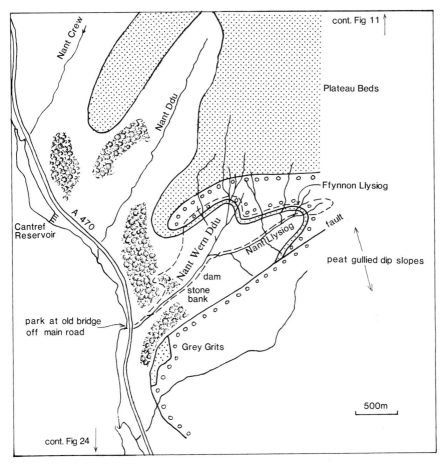

22   Nant Wern Ddu & Nant Llysiog.

on Exmoor has a similar physiography, and there the flash flood disaster of 1952 was the result.

About half-way up towards the junction with the Nant Llysiog, note the remains of a low dam, another 1950's measure designed to break the power of flash floods. The debris accumulated behind it shows how boulders were held back until enough had accumulated to raise the stream bed to the same level as the rim of the dam. The next flood was then able to concentrate its full force on the rim and to breach it. Since then the stream has gradually reworked and removed the deposit built up behind the dam.

At the junction of the stream the slopes between the Nant Wern Ddu and the Nant Llysiog are all in unconsolidated material, part in fact of a large landslip, remnants of which also occur north of the Nant Wern Ddu. Note how the debris from the Nant Llysiog pushes out into the course of the Nant Wern Ddu.

Continue up the Nant Llysiog, following the north bank. Strike streams such as this one "slip into" the landscape, migrating sideways, down the rock dip, and the Llysiog illustrates this well, with solid rock exposures on its southern side, page 26. There are also good examples of arcuate slips on the higher slopes and, after heavy rain, swathes of flattened grass where temporary springs have flowed down the hillsides.

Eventually, near the top of the valley, the walker reaches the upper limit of both the landslip and the Brownstones and a series of interlocking spurs and two waterfalls mark the outcrops of the Plateau Beds and the Grey Grits. The local dip of the rocks is about 5° S.SE but on the south side of the valley-head there is a dip of the same amount to the north. This represents cambering, in response to the erosion of the valley.

A spring known as Ffynnon Llysiog issues in the banks of the last tributary on the north side as the walker ascends the Llysiog. It emerges from the base of the Grey Grits and is a ferruginous spring, reputedly good for the liver. People from the coalfield used to climb up to it, hoping to benefit from drinking its waters. Similar springs occur elsewhere in the district, also at the base of the Grey Grits, e.g. Cwm Callan in the Tâf Fechan. One south of Blaen Callan Farm was tried for umber, and another 450m SW of the farm contains sulphides and iron salts and at one time enjoyed quite a local reputation.

On the plateau top above, the exposures are covered by 3m of peat. Once up there, observe the southern side of the valley. Looking away south-westwards, it is paralleled by one of the northern boundary faults of the Neath Disturbance, Figure 22. Down-throwing to the south, the movement along it is just sufficient to carry down the outcrop of the Plateau Beds and bring the Grey Grits into contact with the Brownstones.

Walk across the plateau top towards a small clump of willow bushes ahead. In places the peat provides good examples of quaking bogs. Accumulated in post-glacial times between 3,000 and 500 years B.C., when the climate was warmer than it is today, the peat is now wasting. There are several branching but enclosed gully systems within it, with good water flow revealing the amount of water movement within the deposits. After extensive dry spells the peat will lose some of this water and be able to absorb subsequent heavy rainfalls. It is when the peat is already saturated and heavy downpours occur that flash floods into the neighbouring valley can be generated. The gully walls show good examples of the present vegetation cover being undermined and toppling in as the peat wastes away, and, for those who search diligently, there are also occasional examples of rotational failure.

Cross NW to reach the plateau edge again at the head of the Nant Wern Ddu where there are more small waterfalls and interlocking spurs as the Grey Grits and Plateau Beds reappear from beneath the blanket of peat. There is also a superb view down the flood tract, with the deflection of the Wern Ddu at the mouth of the Llysiog and the meanders beyond.

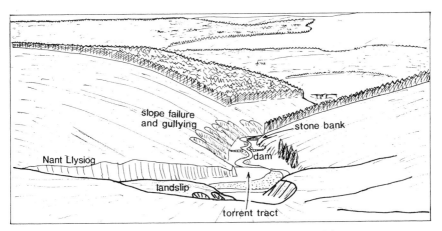

23   View down the Torrent Tract of Nant Wern Ddu.

Retreating falls and peat hags mark the emerging springs which feed the head of the Wern Ddu. Continue around the northern slopes and aim for the centre of the woodland in the distance to the west. On the way, note the small seepage-can failures along the foot of the slopes close to the flood tract, below left. A rough upper limit can be observed for these arcuate hollows, which are developed in the superficial cover of the slopes and controlled partly by seepage and partly by oversteepening at the foot of the slope, as it is cut back laterally by successive flash floods.

Look for a stile situated in the middle of the woodland boundary. This leads to a track through the woodland, switchbacking left to regain the field gate near Pont Llysiog from which the walk began.

Garwnant Forestry Centre to Cader Fawr

From the A470 turn west at the head of the Llwyn-On reservoir and, after crossing the Tâf, fork right, up to the Garwnant Forestry Centre. From the centre there are superb views down valley, the eastern slopes revealing the incoming of the Carboniferous Limestone — first on the ridge tops, then, with the south-southeasterly dip, gradually descending the valley-side in the impressive cliff of Darren Fach, whose great bank of eroded scree tumbles away from the vertical face right down to the edge of the A470.

These are not the nearest exposures of limestone to the viewpoint however. Clearly, the rising outcrop of the beds observed at Daren Fach should mean that further north the limestone horizons would be too high to appear in the present landscape at all. Not so, however, if there is faulting, and this is the answer. Figure 3 shows how we must not be misled by the present land surface, which is a relatively modern feature of the area. If we go back to the situation hundreds of millions of years ago when the limestone outcrop did continue further north over the Old Red Sandstone, then we can begin to understand the problem.

43

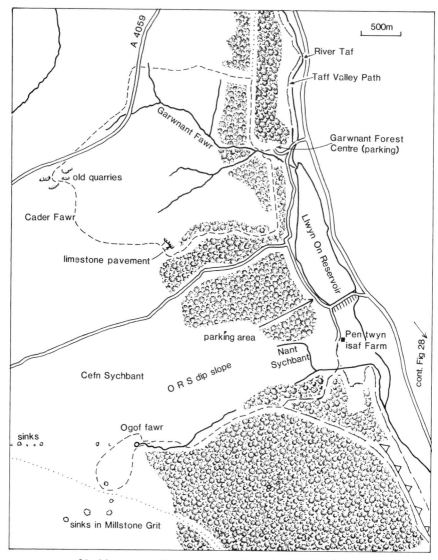

24 Itinerary map for excursions to Cader Fawr and Ogof Fawr.

Part of the northerly extension of the limestones was affected by faulting, along the line of the Neath Disturbance, and the result was that a block of limestone beds was dropped into a lower position. Now, as in Figure 3, put in the modern landscape surface and we can see how the downfaulted block now appears well beyond the remaining main limestone outcrop. Figure 2 shows how Llwyn On reservoir lies right across the fault line which is part of the Neath Disturbance. Note also that the southern margin of the disturbance here is marked by two faults.

Returning our attention to the view from the centre, notice how the slopes around Llwyn-On give little hint of the presence of this structural disturbance. This is not so in other areas of our present study, as will be seen later.

Garwnant Centre stands on the highest unit of the Old Red Sandstones. Coming across the river, the steep increase in gradient takes the approach road up over the Plateau Beds and, at the centre itself, onto the Grey Grits.

From the centre, walk southwest across the Garwnant Fawr valley which notches back the cover of Grey Grits and has lower slopes in the Plateau Beds. At the base of the Grey Grits here there is a plant-bearing mudstone and lingulid brachiopods may be found. On the far side, the track regains the forestry road around the head of the valley and runs over Grey Grits. Follow this road southward for about 1km until it bends right and there is open moorland on that side. Almost on the bend the northern boundary fault of the Neath Disturbance is crossed and from then on, up through the woodland, the walker is on downthrown Carboniferous Limestone. Shortly after the bend, turn off right through the woodland and follow the margin of the wood, or take areas which have been cut to make a pathway, up to 990120.

At 990120, hard by the forest boundary, outcrops of solution-weathered limestones provide a more open vantage point with views north and north-east. These limestones are oolitic, overlying the main limestone (they are part of the Llandyfan Limestone, see succession, page 17). Superb karst solution

25   Weathering of Limestone Outcrop at 990120.

features and small limestone pavements have been etched into them, and encouraged by erosion of the slopes below, major joints have opened up, displaying cambering and toppling features.

Walk westwards up the summit of Cader Fawr. Splay faults of the Neath Disturbance cross the route, altering the levels of the Carboniferous Limestone so that the walker, though going upwards in elevation, finds himself back on the Grey Grits, then on the main limestone (Cil yr Ychen beds), and so up the sequence again to a small capping only of the Llandyfan oolite on the very summit of Cader Fawr. The details of this area should be followed on the 1:50,000 geological map, sheet 231.

What a splendid and unexpected vantage point Cader Fawr is, 978123. Its 60m height above its immediate surroundings gives it an enormous panorama over the Tâf Fawr, with the whole of the eastern valley side visible, the southerly dip, the ridge-top surface controlled by the Plateau Beds and the incoming of the Carboniferous Limestone at Darren Fach and Cefn Cil-Sanws further south, 024104. The previously described Nant Crew, Nant Ddu and Nant Wern Ddu/Nant Llysiog valleys are readily identified.

To the west, a distant view right down the line of the Neath Disturbance and the Neath valley includes the western Fans and the distinctive cone-shaped coal tip between Ystradgynlais and Gwaun-Cae-Gurwen, 25kms away.

The slopes of Cader Fawr have been much quarried and the hill was once an important lime-burning centre. The stone sought was the main limestone of the slopes rather than the oolite capping of the summit itself. Ruins of many old limekilns can be located, most reduced to the point where only a trace of the circular well can be seen, with adjacent pits marking the position of the flue arches.

The summit of the hill is really a S.SE sloping bedding plane in the oolitic limestone, a limestone pavement, just covered with vegetation and, like so

26   Reconstruction of Limeburning at the Kilns on Cader Fawr.

many of our upland surfaces, revealing that a relatively small decrease in temperature would soon produce extensive bare rock, tundra-like landscapes. Walk northwards from the summit. Larger quarries were dug on that side of the hill and tracks link them to the A4059.

Follow the road north-east to 986141 where a path leads east across Pant y Wern to the forestry plantations. Continue east and rejoin a forestry road. Turn south along it to return to the Garwnant Forestry Centre.

Garwnant Forestry Centre along Llwyn-On Reservoir

An all-level walk can be made from the centre by following the road along the west shore of the reservoir. It is a scenic walk rather than a geological one (if the two can ever be regarded as separate interests!) but it provides views of the marshy sedimentation taking place at the head of the reservoir.

Rivers regard reservoirs as lakes and, geologically speaking, these are very temporary phenomena. No sooner are they in existence, whether from man-made causes or natural ones, than rivers begin to deposit sediment in them and to fill them up. Extensive forestry to control run-off and other measures to reduce flash floods, plus the presence of two other reservoirs higher up valley, means that the amount of sediment brought to the Llwyn-On area of the Tâf has been greatly reduced in the last century. Nevertheless the material supplied to it from the Nant Wern Ddu/Nant Llysiog and the Nant Ddu, which enter the river below the previous reservoir (Cantref), is available for deposition in delta fashion at the head of Llwyn-On.

At the right bend in the road, 004125, the lake shore rocks change from the Plateau Beds to the Grey Grits and soon the walker crosses the northern fault of the Neath Disturbance and onto Carboniferous Limestone; Lower Limestone Shales below the road, Abercriban oolites above it. The disturbance is crossed by the time the lakeside road reaches the Nant Abernant at 004117, and the rest of the route down to the picnic site near the dam is back on the Brownstones of the Old Red Sandstone.

Llwyn-On Dam to Nant Sychbant and Ogof Fawr

Start at the car park and picnic site west of the Llwyn-On dam, 008113 (N.B. the parking sign on the O.S. 1:25,000 map is wrongly positioned, too far south). Walk south, up the lane to Pen-twyn-isaf Farm, following part of the main Tâf Valley Path, going through the farm and across the field beyond. Keep on the track as it enters the forestry plantations and bears upwards to the right. At 002101 take the forest road leading west and then south-west, which parallels the boundary of the forest, just a short distance inside the plantations.

Several forest rides lead down to the boundary with the open moor to the north. The forest margin follows the Nant Sychbant valley but the stream only drains the eastern end of the feature. In the centre there is undecided drainage and marshland, marking the outcrop of the Lower Limestone Shales, and then, as the forest boundary is followed westwards, another stream occupies the valley, the Nant Cadlan, flowing away south-westwards.

Follow the forest margin to a stile and then along the banks of the stream. Here the Lower Limestone Shale outcrop is displaced northwards by a NW-SE fault, about 450m east of the sink. The stream continues onto Abercriban Oolites, with the overlying calcite-mudstones of the Llanelly Formation high up on its southern bank. At 985096 the stream disappears into the oolites in a limestone sink and large depression. This is one of the best limestone sinks in the Brecon Beacons, better than those to be seen east of the Tâf Fechan, page 71. Part of the disappearance here is known as Ogof Fawr but the name (Big Cave) is rather a misnomer. Undoubtedly there are cave passages beyond but the amount which can be explored is only a few metres long. The southerly dip of the rocks is well illustrated around the sink and the Llanelly Formation calcite-mudstones can be traced above, on the southern side.

Climb out onto the west side and examine the dry valley beyond. It is pock-marked by many abandoned swallow holes. Marshy ground begins again 0.5km west but no stream emerges for another 0.7km again, and it is not the same stream! Theophilus Jones (see below) ascribed the numerous limestone sinks not to solution but to the limestones being heated at some

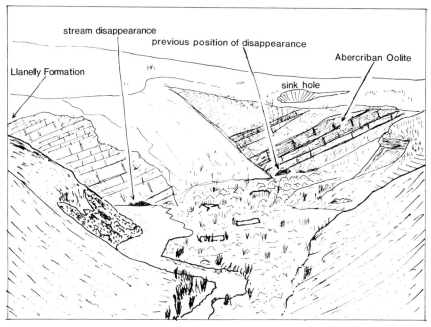

27 Stream Disappearance at Ogof Fawr.

time, then, during a rainstorm producing an effervescence (as when lime is thrown on water), forming huge bubbles which, on bursting, would leave the concave depressions!

Huge seasonal starling roosts can sometimes be observed in the vicinity of Ogof Fawr.

Darren Fach, Darren Fawr and Cefn Cil-Sanws

Driving northwards up the A470 from Merthyr Tydfil, the huge limestone screes and the cliff section of Cil yr Ychen Limestone above form the first spectacular scenery of the national park. The limestone was quarried at Danydarren, 025091, near the southern end but old limekilns adjacent to the road show how the screes have also been used for limeburning.

Looking across the Tâf valley from the road below Darren Fach, there is a fine view of the crags opposite, Craig Penmaillard, page 28. It is interesting to recall the account of Theophilus Jones. In his *"A History of the County of Brecknock"*, 1911, he wrote how the strata on opposite sides of the river here "from their similar shape and position . . . seem to have been neighbours, much nearer than they are at present . . . evidently display the marks and ravages of an earthquake and it is by no means improbable that, elevated as the precipices appear to the traveller in the vale below, the river Tâf at one time ran over their very summit, where, forming a small channel and consequently a fissure, it may have conduced towards their disseveration . . . We think the progress of this phenomenon (the earthquake) may be traced with tolerable accuracy; its principal direction was from east to west, its effects are first observable in the county near Pontneathvaughan where it tore the Dinas rock from its foundation and whirled it into its present fantastical shape and position . . ." (He was certainly a catastrophist *par excellence*!) . . . "As it proceeded eastwards . . . entering the vale of Tâf Fawr a less weighty stratum of stone occurred near the surface and, below, the soil was of a loose and crumbling composition, as seen by the sections on both sides of the vale when travelling from Merthyr . . . and here the throes of agonising nature . . . loudly and forcibly . . . groans . . . tearing asunder the rocks now called Graig Fawr" (Darren Fawr) "and Penmaillard, then united, the convulsion formed the present vale of Tâf and precipitated the river into a chasm at least 100 yards below; the explosion or rather the steam arising from it, as it rent the rocks on each side, threw large fragments of them into a confused heap in the manner in which they appear as we begin to descend to Coed y Cymmer" (ie, by Darren Fach) "and left scattered upon the surface those immense masses . . . of plum-pudding stone" (Millstone Grit) "slaked lime, rubbish and earth . . . lying . . . below the upper stratum or wall of rock on which the action of fire is evidently discernible".

Theophilus Jones was evidently looking up at the Darren rock faces and the natural weathering stains visible on them. He was a real catastrophist, and while catastrophes do undoubtedly occur in geological history, many processes are imperceptibly gradual, so slow that it is only when they are measured against the million of years for which they may continue that they are seen to achieve any considerable effect.

Jones was not totally wrong. He saw that great earth movements had affected the Pont Nedd Fechan area, part in fact of the Neath Disturbance, but he wrongly traced the fault east to this part of the Tâf Fawr valley, rather than where it really crosses the river at the Llwyn On reservoir. He did not describe the feature as a fault. However, he was right in recognising the Tâf as a superimposed river, cutting down from above, in its passage into the northern rim of the coalfield, although at its southern exit from the same structure in the Tâf Gorge at Castell Coch he was back to his single

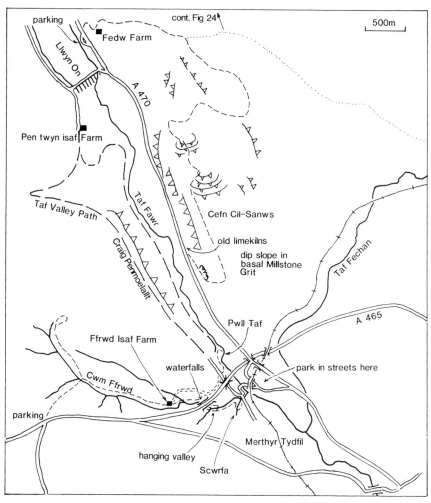

28   Itinerary map for excursions to Cwm Ffrwd and Cefn Cil-Sanws.

enormous earthquake theory. Faults are indicated in the Tâf valley both here to the north of Merthyr and in the gorge to the south, and there may well have been earthquakes at each small movement along them in the past, but there has not been a single catastrophic event as Jones described.

Around Darren Fach and on the hillside above, a complete succession from Brownstones up through Plateau Beds and Grey Grits, through the Carboniferous Limestone series and eventually onto Basal Grits of the Millstone Grit series is present. However, along the A470 route, the valleyside is so steep that the huge pile of screes has covered all the beds below the main (Cil yr Ychen) limestone.

Drive further north to the lay-by at 010118, on the west side of the road. Cross the road to the track up to Fedw Farm. This is a public footpath. Turn left by the farm buildings and up the track eastwards between forestry plantation on to the open moorland.

The right-of-way leads east over the col between Garn Ddu and Coedcae'r Gwartheg and by making a wide loop east and south it is possible to get round the enclosed fields of Coedcae'r Gwartheg and Coedcae'r Ychain onto the outcrops of the hilltops east of Darren Fach. On no account approach the edge of Darren Fach but, towards the side of the summits, notice the very large displaced blocks of rock which were probably slid down the bedding planes in glacial times.

Figure 28 shows the geology of the walk. Continue south down the ridge of Cefn Cil-Sanws, noting the change onto the Basal Grits of the Millstone Grit series, to 027090 where a right of way down through Danydarren quarry can be gained, and on NW down to the A470 and a stile at Wyrlod Ddu, 023094.

Cwm Ffrwd

The Ffrwd is the last major right bank tributary of the Tâf Fawr before its confluence with the Tâf Fechan. The valley drains part of the Millstone Grit dip-slope and can be examined in two sections, these being divided, at the point where the Heads of the Valleys road (A465) crosses high over the stream, by a waterfall which can only be ascended in dry summer weather.

For the lower part of the valley start west of Cefn-Coed-y-Cymmer, at the little bridge in Pontycapel Road, 030076. Steps lead down into the river bed on the upstream side of the bridge and in low water periods it is possible to walk up the river bed. Generally however it is best to cross the bridge to a stile just beyond the cottage and follow a track up through the fields, climbing south-westwards towards the electricity transmission lines. The path in fact ascends the south bank of a tributary of the Ffrwd known as the Scwrfa (the Scouring Brook). Head for the spot where the transmission line crosses this valley. A water pipe crosses the stream at the same place.

Above and below this site the Scwrfa is a very different stream. Up-valley its gradient is more gentle, the valley more open. This area was once a pond,

51

dammed up close to where the water pipe now crosses. Periodically the impounded waters were released to rush down the much steeper section downstream and scour out ironstone nodules from the banks — hence the name Scwrfa.

A thick sandstone bed marks the notch between the two different section of the brook. It is a quartzite, the Cumbriense Quartzite. In the steep section below, two marine bands, horizons marking marine submergence of the Millstone Grit deltaic sediments, can be found. Below the sandstone lies the outcrop of the *Gastrioceras cumbriense* marine band. Containing the coiled-shelled goniatite of that name, the band is the first one seen when descending the stream. Nearer the junction with the Ffrwd lies the *Gastrioceras cancellatum* band. To examine the steep lower section, cross the brook near the water pipeline and take a path westwards down into the Ffrwd, then return to the lower part of the Scwrfa. Alternatively continue on up the Ffrwd itself. Wellington boots are useful here for the stream must be forded several times.

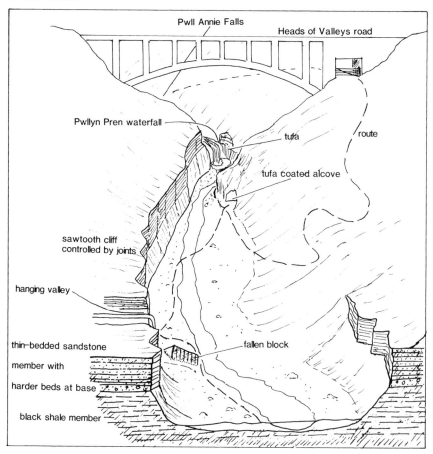

29   Cwm Ffrwd; the lower valley, looking west.

About 200m upstream the valley widens. Wherever they are undercut by the stream, the banks reveal black shales of the Millstone Grit beds. Figure 29 shows the nature of the valley. A river cliff on the south bank near 027705 has been trimmed away on the outer side of a bend in the stream. In the rocky alcove above the bend a large pendulous mass of calcareous tufa is forming. (Tufa becomes important further upstream, especially on the north bank, and its origins are discussed below).

To the right of the tufa, a fault cuts the bank and upthrows both the black shales near the river and an overlying group of thin-bedded sandstones. The fault is marked by a high narrow earthy alcove, and groups of more steeply dipping shales.

Notice how the valley is controlled by the two groups of beds, generally forming graded slopes in the softer black shales, and cliffs in the thin-bedded sandstone group. Nearing a hanging valley and waterfall where a tributary plunges into the Ffrwd, the upper sandstone-bedded cliff is marked by two prominent joint directions which have allowed it to erode into a saw-tooth pattern. Blocks of sandstones become undermined and fall from between the converging joints. A fallen group can be seen just by the foot of the waterfall.

Beyond the fall the lower cliff is also exposed, its black shales clearly less well-laminated than the sandstones above. A marked division between the two can be traced along the middle of the cliff, formed by a more resistant sandstone horizon which is responsible for the valley's waterfalls. Notice how the well-defined joints of the upper sandstone group become less noticeable as they are traced down into the shale group beneath. The joints also become less planar and curve downwards towards the north-east.

Upstream, beneath the graceful span of the Heads of the Valleys road viaduct, the river becomes more narrowly enclosed and surrounded by high cliffs. These are encrusted with calcareous tufa. Great creepers of ivy dangle from overhead and hundreds of water seepages feed moss-covered walls or splash from rocky overhangs. In the roof of a small alcove at the base of the north bank the tufa forms stalactite curtains.

But this is Millstone Grit country! Why is there so much lime in these waters? And why is there more tufa formation on the north bank of the Ffrwd than on the south? The tufa on the north side is more readily explained, Figure 30. Lime-bearing groundwaters, flowing down the dip of the limestone beds outcropping to the north, enter the overlying but topographically lower placed Millstone Grits and emerge in the north bank seepages of the deeply incised Ffrwd.

A possible explanation of the tufa on the south side of the valley involves conditions during the Ice Age. Seepage into the Ffrwd today soon fills it with superb ice stalactites in winter. In the Ice Age the valley would have become filled with stagnant ice, enabling glacial drift from the north to be carried over onto the southern side. A fair proportion of limestone fragments in that drift would account for the lime in solution now dripping in on the southern valleyside. Examination of drift material on the surface south of the Ffrwd does not reveal many limestone fragments today, but that is to be expected. Limestone is a soluble rock, and even though it has contributed to a drift deposit, it will subsequently be removed as a calcareous solution.

Continue into the alcove of the lower waterfall, Pwllyn Pren. In low summer flow it is possible to cross the plunge pool by keeping to the right hand (north) side and ascend the fall over rough lumpy tufa deposits. In winter the plunge pool is too deep and the explorer must return some way down-valley before it is possible to ascend the valleyside into the fields to the north, Figure 29. Thus the walk can be continued upstream, passing beneath the Heads of the Valleys road viaduct. From the viaduct there is a fine "aerial" view of the tufa-encrusted alcove of the lower falls, and in winter to the upper falls beyond. Walk northwards from the road and examine the upper falls, Pwll Annie. They are higher, and the lip of these falls is

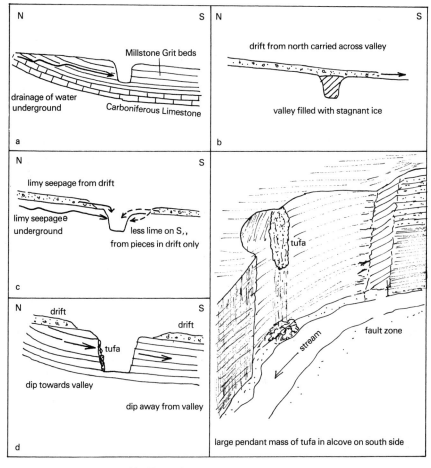

30   Formation of Tufa in Cwm Ffrwd.

controlled by the hard quartzite beds (Cumbriense Quartzite) seen previously in the Scwrfa brook. Several small tributaries also produce waterfalls in the upper Ffrwd, their hanging valleys unable to match the main stream's deeply cut chasm.

In the headwaters of the Ffrwd there are further interesting geological sections. There is no public pathway up the entire length of the stream. Its headwaters can be reached by taking the lane beneath the Heads of the Valleys road viaduct at 028078. This lane is the southern end of the main Tâf Valley Path described on page 28. Incidentally, there is a lay-by on the Heads of the Valleys road just west of this viaduct which can be used as a parking spot for the more westerly viaduct over the Ffrwd, but the 375m walk back to the latter needs care!

Just after passing 028078 beneath the Tâf viaduct, a track to Ffrwd Isaf Farm begins on the left. Permission is necessary to use this, but at the farm a stile leads into fields and a track up the north bank of the stream.

31   Cwm Ffrwd in winter when the tufa-forming seepages create gigantic icicles.
John Yates

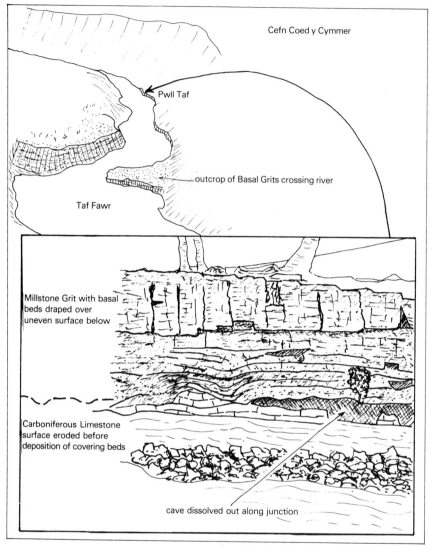

Cefn Coed y Cymmer

Pwll Taf

outcrop of Basal Grits crossing river

Taf Fawr

Millstone Grit with basal beds draped over uneven surface below

Carboniferous Limestone surface eroded before deposition of covering beds

cave dissolved out along junction

32 Pwll Tâf and the unconformity between the Carboniferous Limestone and the Millstone Grit.

Alternatively travel along the Heads of the Valleys road to the parking area at the hotel, 005074, and walk north over open land, aiming for the orange marker north of the Ffrwd which indicates where the gas pipeline crosses the valley. The sections begin close to this and in a series of exposures on both banks reveal Millstone Grit beds:

Flaggy mudstones	1.5m
Silty mudstones	2.0m
Mudstone with fish fragments	1.5m
Pale grey mudstone with thin ironstone bands	4.8m

Mudstone with *Lingula* and fish fragments   1.8m

Mudstone with abundant *Carbonicola* species in upper part   2.4m

Follow the edge of the wood up onto the plateau above the eastern headwater. Extensive views show fine dip-slopes of Carboniferous Limestone and Millstone Grit to the east on Darren and Cefn Cil-Sanws with no hint of the deep cwm of the Tâf in between, and southward to the ironstone and coal working scarred slopes of Mynydd Aberdâr. South-eastwards the Coal Measure shale lowland around Merthyr Tydfil is prominent, and the dip of the Coal Measures and their sandstone beds along the slopes of the Tâf valley below the town can be seen.

Cwm Tâf Fawr

There is one outstanding feature in Cwm Tâf which should not be missed by anyone exploring the geology of the district. Again, follow the lane up below the Tâf viaduct of the Heads of the Valleys road. Passing beneath the latter at 028078, about 40m beyond, opposite the track into Ffrwd Isaf Farm, cross the stile and walk over to the edge of the field overlooking the river. A path leads north along the edge of the field, continuing along the edge of the woodland beyond and dropping down on to the grassy flat by the bend in the Tâf at 027082. Here an outcrop of Millstone Grit Basal Grits, full of white quartz pebbles, forms a barrier across the stream and marks the line of an old wooden railway viaduct that crossed the river here.

As their name implies, the Basal Grits lie right at the bottom of the Millstone Grit beds and the underlying Carboniferous Limestone is exposed on the opposite bank of the river a short distance upstream. The limestones are seen almost at river level, with Basal Grits forming the rest of the river cliff above. The grit beds appear to be folded near their base.

The fold-like features are due to erosion of the Carboniferous Limestone surface however. This occurred before the deposition of the Basal Grits, which were then draped over the irregularities of the limestone surface. In the present-day landscape the top of the limestones has again been eroded, this time by solution to form a long low cave. It is known as Pwll Tâf.

Walkers following the lower route of the main Tâf Valley Path can continue upstream from this locality.

The Tâf Fechan Valley

The walks described in the Tâf Fechan concentrate on those areas which further illustrate the geology of the district. Many other attractive walks exist, but cover features already described, eg, from the Neuadd reservoirs up the old Roman road to Cribin and the main escarpment, or again, around the watershed with the Usk at Torpantau, where there are fine waterfall features to be seen.

Cwm Callan and Bryniau Gleision

Turn off the Pontsticill to Torpantau road at 065143 on the west side of the Pontsticill reservoir and drive over the bridge separating the upper and lower areas of the lake. Park by the roadside beyond; turning space is available just before the old railway bridge further along the lane, but do not park there or up the lane beyond.

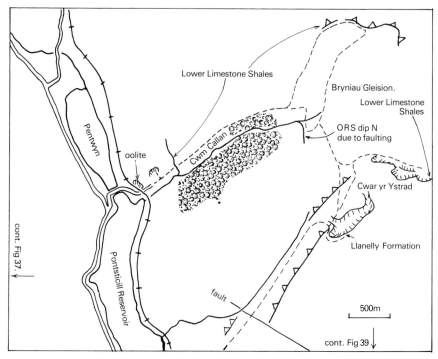

33   Itinerary map for Cwm Callan, Neath Disturbance.

This locality is within the downfaulted block of the Neath Disturbance and the cutting by the old railway station exposes the oolitic (Abercriban) limestones. Follow the lane up towards the Dolygaer Outdoor Pursuits Centre. A short diversion up the north bank tributary to 063147 provides an exposure of the Lower Limestone Shales at the base of the Carboniferous Limestone.

The south side of Cwm Callan is largely outside the faulted zone and its Brownstone beds should follow the regional dip, away from the observer towards the S.SE. However, due to the presence of the disturbance the dip has been reversed and is locally northward, towards the Cwm Callan. Continue up the lane passing the ruins of Blaen Callan Farm and on to the open moor (see page 42 for details of the mineral springs near the farm). Cross south to the gullies on the far side of Cwm Callan. There the northward dip of the Brownstones is well exposed, eg. 078153.

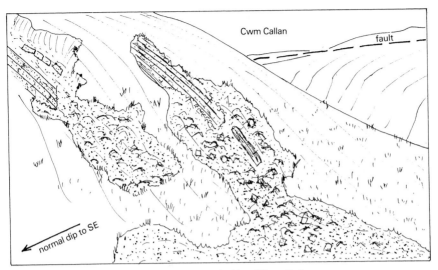

34 Gully on the south side of Cwm Callan.

Returning across the stream and continuing northwards, examine the area of Bryniau Gleision. This little rounded hill is another downfaulted part of the Neath Disturbance. Limestones are exposed in crags adjacent to the stream on the south side. The "core" of the hill is of Carboniferous sandstones, locally developed within the Cil yr Ychen Limestone.

More gullies to the south can be explored from here, and an interesting feature are the pebbles of Carboniferous Limestone which occur in them. Derived by erosion from the main outcrop to the south and carried down into these gullies, they are curiously polished by the waters from the Old Red Sandstone. The polish is only skin deep but it does bring out their oolitic structure beautifully.

Those who wish to make a circular walk in the Pontsticill area can continue south to the quarries at Cwar yr Ystrad.

Cwar yr Ystrad Quarries

Cwar yr Ystrad is a long NE-SW trending natural escarpment of Carboniferous Limestone high up on the hills which form the eastern watershed of the Tâf Fechan. A large quarry has been developed at the northern end of the escarpment, cut back into dolomite at the top of the Lower Limestone Shales, Abercriban Oolite, the main Cil yr Ychen limestone and the Llanelly Formation. The latter is well-exposed at the southern end of the disused part of the quarries, where coarse fibrous calcite nodules up to 20cm in diameter are a feature of it. They form a readily identifiable bed in the cleared area at the top of the eastern face of the quarry, southern end. A fine bed, crowded with rounded algal balls (oncolites) occurs about 1m below the fibrous calcite nodule bed while about the same distance above it there is another containing larger oncolites of the species *Uraloporella*. The oncolites form around small pieces of rock or shell which are being rolled around on the sea bed. Oolitic limestones and calcite-mudstones can also be studied in this quarry.

The NW-SE trending Tredegar Fault throws the outcrops down as the walker works round to the next group of quarries above Blaen Duffryn Crawnon. The fault is crossed between the two quarry areas. A feature of the second group is the exposure of the Lower Limestone Shales, rich in brachiopods, at approximately 096147, by the quarry road close to the entrance at the eastern end.

Returning to the escarpment of Cwar yr Ystrad, note the bridleway which runs below it on the 1:25,000 map. A second small scarp just west of the bridleway is of interest. It extends from 084147 to 079142. It marks the base of the Carboniferous Limestone outcrops, a limestone at the base of the Lower Limestone Shales. The bed weathers to a very honeycombed appearance. The locality shows how, in the absence of rock exposures, geological boundaries may be mapped from other features, such as vegetation. On the limestone outcrop the grass is the typical close sward, but to the west of the boundary a rough molinia grass covers the underlying Old Red Sandstone. Follow the boundary southwestwards beyond the escarpment. The contrast in the grassland confirms its course and the Lower Limestone Shale outcrop is followed by the Cwm Criban stream as far as 070130, where it turns west, down faulted slopes to reach the Pontsticill reservoir.

The effect of the faulting is most noticeable in the higher slopes to the east, with the sudden termination of the lines of limestone crags. The bridlepath should be continued southwestwards where it eventually leads down to the road south of Pontsticill Dam or, if desired, links up with the itinerary for the Baltic and Twynau Gwynion quarries, page 64.

Nant Car Fach

A walk in the Nant Car Fach area west of the Pontsticill reservoir provides a fine opportunity to study some of the close relationships between the tributaries of the Tâf Fechan and the Tâf Fawr and the alignment of the Neath Disturbance, Figure 35.

Comparison of the 1:25,000 map (Brecon Beacons National Park, Central Sheet) with the 1:50,000 solid geological map (Merthyr Tydfil sheet, no. 231) shows how the middle portion of the Nant Rhyd-ddu/Nant Car Fach stream is cut along the southern boundary fault of the disturbance, from 035136 to 045139.

In two other areas stream courses run parallel to faults, but their relationship is less obvious. The two cases are the Cwm Callan stream, coming in on the east side of the Pontsticill reservoir (to the Tâf Fechan) and

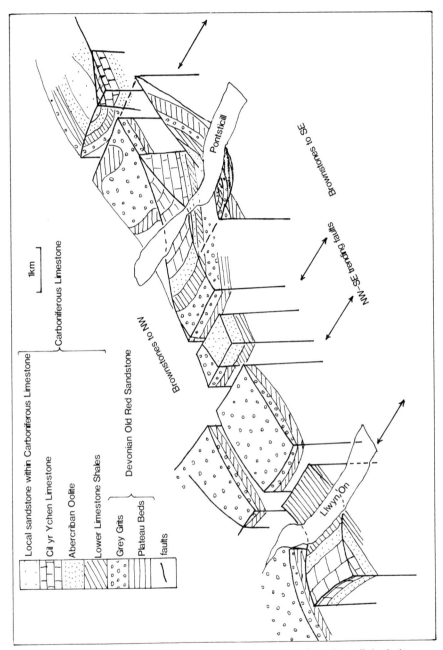

1km

Local sandstone within Carboniferous Limestone

Cil yr Ychen Limestone

Abercriban Oolite

Lower Limestone Shales

Grey Grits

Plateau Beds

faults

Carboniferous Limestone

Devonian Old Red Sandstone

Brownstones to NW

Brownstones to SE

NW-SE trending faults

Pontsticill

Llwyn On

35   An "exploded" view of the Neath Disturbance, opened up along all the faults.

the Nant Car, flowing down to the east shore of Llwyn On reservoir (to the Tâf Fawr). Together with the middle portion of the Nant Car Fach already described, these streams form a striking NE-SW alignment on the 1:25,000 map.

Notice the dip arrows on the geological map in the case of both the Cwm Callan and the Nant Car. They show that the rocks dip north, away from the fault in both cases. Figure 36 offers an explanation of the relationship

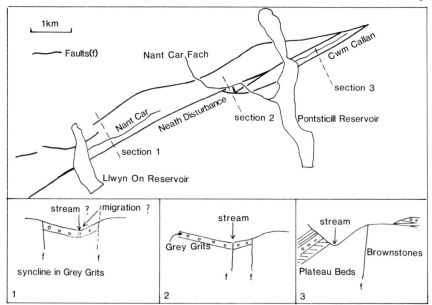

36 Relationship of streams and faulting along the Neath Disturbance.

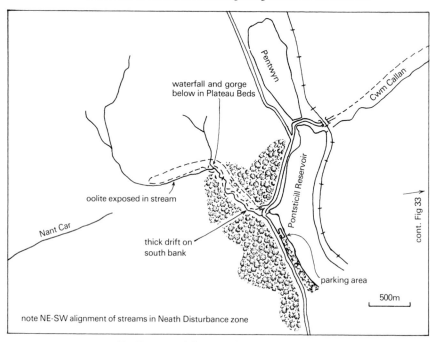

37 Features of the Nant Car Fach itinerary.

between stream and fault; the streams began cutting their valleys at a higher level than the present land surface and used the line of weakness represented by the fault. But, as they cut down, so the effect of the local northward dips began to deflect them off the fault-line, making them migrate laterally to their present positions.

For the Nant Car walk, park at a recently built picnic site on the west side of Pontsticill reservoir, near 053132. Walk north along the road to the bend by the small bay. Just north of the bend a forest road climbs steeply up the hillside to the west, then levels out and passes the abandoned house of Cwm Car. Two routes can be chosen, either straight ahead along the forest road to the margin of the wood at 045139 where a stile leads direct over to the Nant Car Fach waterfalls, or following the Nant Car Fach itself up through the woodland.

Following the stream, large fossiliferous blocks of Carboniferous Limestone are soon encountered, washed out of thick glacial drift deposits on the south bank and down from fault-controlled outcrops further up valley. Going on up the stream, it soon becomes enclosed in walls of Plateau Beds, 12.5m of siltstones, mudstones and quartzitic sandstones, purple and grey in colour. It is seldom possible to wade up the stream bed, and the walker must climb over the north or south bank to reach the head of the gorge. However, first notice the form of the gorge. The south wall is crumbling and step-like because the dip on that side is towards the river. On

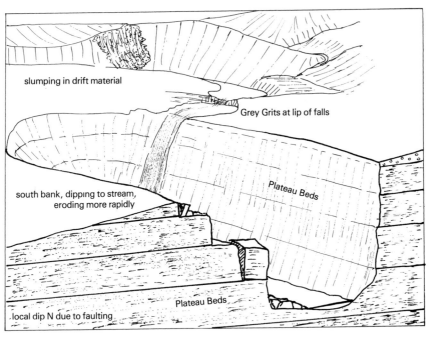

38   Waterfall in Plateau Beds and Grey Grits, in Nant Car Fach.

the north wall however, where the dip is away from the stream, an almost undamaged vertical joint-plane occupies most of the face.

The Nant Car Fach enters the gorge over a fine waterfall. The fall is controlled by a joint-plane running in the same east-west direction as those which have been used to cut the gorge below. Hard quartzitic sandstones interbedded with purple mudstones form the face of the falls, but the rim is capped by Grey Grits. Fish fragments occur 0.6m above the base of the Grey Grits and there are mudstone layers containing plant fragments. The Grey Grit has been downfaulted into this position by the movements along the Neath Disturbance.

Up-valley, sandstone beds at several points in the stream bed show further examples of dips contrary to the expected southerly direction and, about 1km southwestwards, a downfaulted area of Carboniferous Limestone outcrops in the north bank. Marked by large polished blocks of beautifully oolitic structure, the outcrop belongs to the Abercriban Oolite.

Pontsticill Reservoir Dam to Abercriban, Baltic and Twynau Gwynion Quarries and Pwll Morlais

Park near the eastern end of Pontsticill reservoir dam, taking care not to obstruct the junction or access up the east side of the reservoir to the narrow gauge railway station. Alternatively, park in the forestry commission's public car park at 057120, where their long-distance walk begins, and then cross the dam on foot.

There is no right of access to the hillside across the railway line, so, from the reservoir turn south on the road to Pant Cadifor and then left up the footpath which leaves the lane at 061114. The path climbs northeastwards, passing beneath the railway track. Two routes are possible at this point. Either walk a few metres beyond the railway and turn back right, upwards to reach the head of an old inclined plane, still complete with its winding drum, on the edge of Baltic Quarry, or preferably turn sharp right immediately after passing beneath the railway and walk south alongside the track. The latter route provides a more complete succession up through the Carboniferous Limestone of the hillside.

Walking south by the railway, the ruins of an old quarry crushing plant are found on the left, once fed by a huge stone-lined rock chute from the quarries above. By the base of this chute there are small exposures of the Lower Limestone Shales, the limestone beds often crowded with flattened brachiopods.

Climb steeply up the bank to the right side of the rock chute and enter the quarry about 40m above. This is Odynau Tyle'r Bont Quarry. Here beds of dolomitised (brown weathering) and non-dolomitised (grey) limestones alternate in the face. The dolomitisation indicates very shallow marine conditions, often occuring where influxes of freshwater and sea water were mixing. The quarry is still in the Lower Limestone Shales but there are no shale beds at this level.

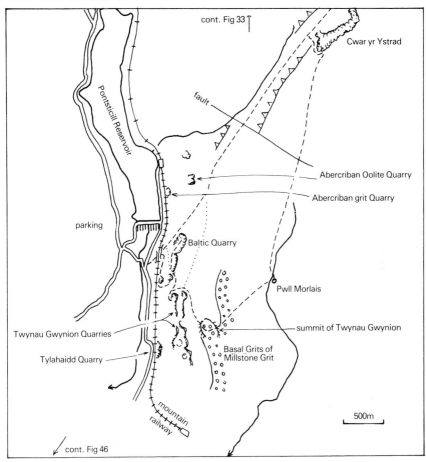

39   Route map for Twynau Gwynion and Cwar yr Ystrad.

From this small quarry again climb steeply on up the right side of the rock chute, to gain the south end of the southern section of Baltic (New Tyle'r Bont) Quarry. Here the Abercriban Oolite forms the main face, with the Llanelly Formation above. The intertidal, shallow marine and muddy facies of the latter are readily identified in many fallen pieces of yellowish-green and pinkish tinged colour. Incidentally, the Llanelly Formation is named from the quarry of that name in the Clydach Valley and not from the town of Llanelly.

Baltic Quarry has a shallow face at its southern end, biting deeper into the hillside beyond. Its exposures are important in the Carboniferous Limestone succession for the junction of the Abercriban Oolite and the Llanelly Formation is marked by an unconformity. Notice a prominent ledge,

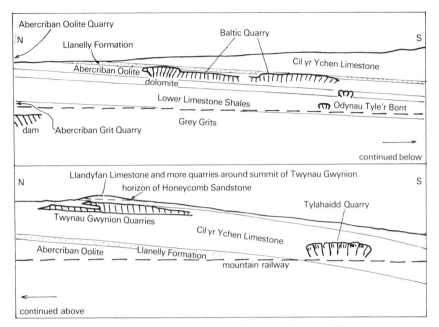

40   Key to Quarries east of Pontsticill as seen from the village.

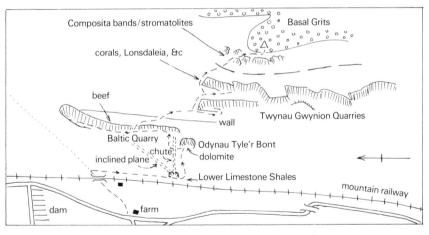

41   Details of the Baltic and Twynau Gwynion Quarries area.

generally about 22m above the quarry floor. This ledge is near the top of the oolite succession and, just about on or above it, there is a boulder bed. This is the bed which indicates an interval of erosion, a period of interruption in the deposition of the rocks, a break in the geological record which is called an unconformity. The shallow marine conditions in which the oolites were being deposited came to a halt and an uplift of the area caused erosion to occur instead.

66

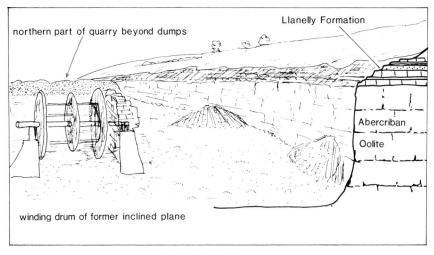

northern part of quarry beyond dumps

Llanelly Formation

Abercriban

Oolite

winding drum of former inclined plane

42   View in Baltic Quarry.

For perhaps several thousand years, the surface of the oolitic limestones below was weathered and eroded, forming karst landscape features. Clay-filled solution pipes and cavities were formed, probably beneath a soil profile. The climate was still humid. Ancient solution surfaces such as this are known as palaeokarst.

Higher parts of the Llanelly Formation show that the climate sometimes reverted to semi-arid conditions again, and several levels reveal intervals of drying out and erosion of the beds, with formation of fossil soils, palaeosols, see Geological Evolution, page 22.

The Succession in Baltic Quarry:

Top of quarry

Llanelly Formation	Light grey calcite-mudstones rich in algal material	7.6m

. . . . Boulder bed . . . . Unconformity . . . .

	Coarse crinoidal limestone with beef at the base	1.8-2.4m
	Calcite-mudstone with algal markings (Lip of ledge where it faces south)	1.8-2.4m
Abercriban Oolite	Coarse oolitic limestone with brachiopods *Camarotoechia* and *Schellwienella*; much dolomitised near base	10.7m
	Shale-mudstone bed	0.75m
	Dark grey oolitic limestone, dolomitic, especially towards the base	6.0m
	Shale-mudstone bed	0.45m
Lower Limestone Shales	Dark, very dolomitic limestone with *Spirifer*	2m seen

The calcite-mudstone and shale-mudstone beds represent periods when the amount of sediment coming into the sea-bed was increased. Algae – the sea plants often formed like mats over the sea bed – aid limestone formation by trapping calcite grains to form laminated limy sediments. If they are seen in this layered fashion in rocks they are called stromatolites (see Twynau Gwynion quarries, below). In contrast, rounded though irregular growths of algae, algal balls, are known as oncolites (see Cwar Ystrad).

The beef found in the topmost beds of the Abercriban Oolite is a fibrous

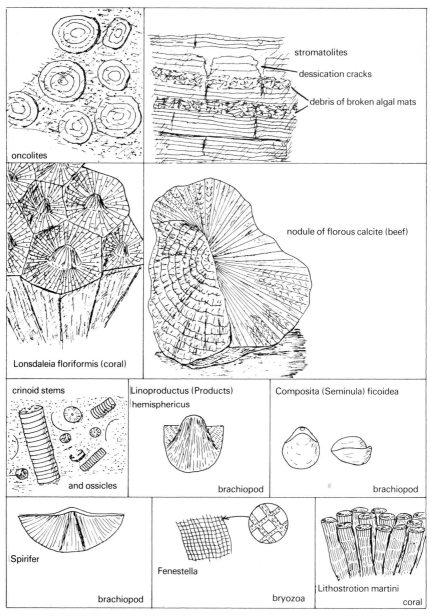

43   Some Features to be found in the Baltic and Twynau Gwynion Quarries.

form of calcite. It occurs in rounded heads of closely packed fibres, and when split open the Baltic Quarry examples are often of a yellowish-green colour.

Proceed through the tramway cutting into the northern part of the quarry, arriving at the winding drum at the top of the inclined plane referred to earlier. In this northern part of the quarry large nodules of beef can be found on the waste dumps towards the far end of the excavation. Walk up between the face and the first dumps and search those immediately beyond. These dumps overlook the deepest part of the operation.

Following old quarry inclines descend to the quarry floor and, where the face allows, examine the screes of waste. Cavities in some blocks reveal terminated quartz crystals, some with fluid inclusions of greenish-yellow colour with small gas bubbles. These may be hydrocarbons for the quartz crystals are often surrounded by black bituminous hydrocarbon (oil) material, and this also accounts for the presence of purple fluorite (Blue John) in some of the local rock joints (see Vaynor Quarry, page 77). These mineral features indicate a phase of hydrothermal mineralisation which was accompanied by migrating hydrocarbon deposits.

From the western edge of the Baltic Quarry floor there is a superb panoramic view, northwards to the main summits of the Beacons, and, following the Tâf Fechan south and west, to the limestone outcrops of Morlais Hill and beyond to the second great escarpment of the region, formed by the resistant sandstones of the Coal Measures, the Pennant Sandstones.

The Abercriban Quarries, from which the Abercriban Oolite is named, lie lower down the slopes to the north, the upper quarry exposing the limestones and the lower one, 063127, near the railway revealing an unbroken sequence of sedimentation from the Plateau Beds up through to the Lower Limestone Shales. Here the final stages of the Old Red Sandstone continent are revealed, and its submergence beneath the Carboniferous seas; red sandstone beds from the southern desert latitudes, then submergence beneath tropical seas as Britain drifted northwards. The southern end of the quarry is hidden in fallen blocks and rubble so the Plateau Beds are difficult to see, but there are fine cross-bedding structures in the Grey Grits. The grits were used in the construction of the Pontsticill reservoir dam, as facings for the rubble filled structure. The beds revealed in the quarry are:

Carboni-ferous	Carboni-ferous Limestone	Lower Limestone Shales	Tough dark grey crinoidal limestone with *Spirifer* brachiopods and the bryozoan *Fenestella*, dolomitised	3.7m
		Grey Grits	Pebbly quartz conglomerate	0.46-3.7m
			Olive coloured shales	Nil-0.9m
Devonian	Upper Old Red Sandstone		Olive coloured hard quartzitic sandstone	10.7m
		Plateau Beds	Red mudstones with fish fragments	

N.B. where two measurements are given the first refers to the southern end of the quarry and the second to the northern.

From the splendid viewpoint of Baltic Quarry work southwards, up hill, to the great line of quarries which fringe the western slopes of Twynau Gwynion from 064111 to 066103. Known as the Odynau Gwynion, the white kilns, these were the limestone quarries for the Rhymney Ironworks and were opened in the main Cil yr Ychen limestone beds. Many old limekilns can be located.

The slopes above the quarries, leading up to the summit triangulation point, are crossed by the horizon of the Honeycomb Sandstone. This is a widely developed and very distinctive bed in the Llandyfan Limestone part of the Carboniferous Limestone succession. It is what geologists call a marker horizon because it clearly identifies where you are in the succession. It marks the base of the topmost fossil zone of the Carboniferous Limestone, the D (Dibunophyllum) zone, and can also be seen in the Tâf Fechan gorge by the Heads of the Valleys road bridge, below.

Do not be misled by the name Honeycomb Sandstone into looking for a bed with a sandy colour and texture. The bed is still rich in limy material and greyish in colour. It is the way the bed weathers that is so distinctive. It is 0.6m thick.

Close to the top of the limestone sequence at Twynau Gwynion, look for the large brachiopod *Productus hemisphericus*. This rather plump individual sat convex valve downward on the sea bed, supporting itself with fleshy

44 Millstone broken during manufacture and left among the screes of Basal Grits east of the summit of Twynau Gwynion. (Photo: Jack Evans)

props, rather like a boat beached and propped up at low tide. The position was an unstable one and after death was seldom maintained, the fossil being overturned to convex upward position, so, a good illustration of preservation in growth position and death position can be obtained then, if specimens in both states can be located.

Some of the westward-facing sections of limestone near the hilltop have weathered sufficiently to reveal that they are built of undulating, nearly horizontal layers of algae, ie, they are stromatolites.

Shortly before the summit triangulation point is reached, the Carboniferous Limestone sequence ends and the top of the hill and the southerly dip-slope are capped by the Basal Grit of the Millstone Grit succession. The grits vary from obviously quartz pebble-rich beds to ones of thick-bedded sandstones or quartzite, but the former are dominant here.

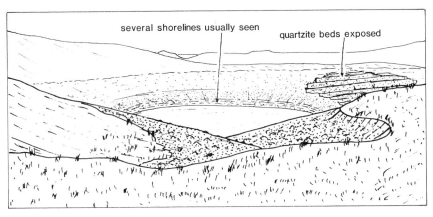

45 Pwll Morlais, a sink in Millstone Grit beds formed by collapse after solution of underlying Carboniferous Limestone beds.

From the summit of Twynau Gwynion walk N.NE across the moors to the Nant Morlais valley which runs south approximately along the junction of the Basal Grits and the Shale Group of the Millstone Grit. On its east bank at 076113 is Pwll Morlais, a fine example of a sink hole, its peaty shore revealing the various previous water levels. Heavy rains increase the pond level and then seepage away into the underlying limestones gradually reduces it again. The feature is one of hundreds of such sinks in South Wales. Produced by solution and collapse of the limestones below, they are common features of the Millstone Grit outcrops, extending upwards into this cover of sandstones and conglomerates by loosening the blocks away along joint systems.

About 1.25km further northeast lies another un-named example, 089121. It is an interesting depression, being a double feature, the dividing wall between the larger and smaller sinks being breached and now almost removed. West of it superb limestone pavements reveal further examples of erosion along joint patterns, the edges of individual beds being gradually frost-heaved away, block by block. They move off, down-slope, in trains of stone stripes, or tumble into nearby sink holes.

Compass bearings are probably the best way of locating both the above, on an otherwise featureless moorland. Alternatively, head north from Twynau Gwynion summit to join the bridle path shown on the 1:25,000 map and follow it to Cwm Criban and the long line of the Cwar yr Ystrad limestone scarp, thus making a loop linking up with the Cwm Callan and Cwar yr Ystrad quarries itinerary previously described.

Morlais Hill and Castle

Several routes are available onto this imposing hill with its fine staircase of quarries along the northern slopes, eg, from sites along Pontsarn Hill where there are access stiles, but it is safest to park cars at the Golf Club (lane entrance from Pantcadifor: car park at 054094). Care is needed while walking on the hill top since much of it forms part of the golf course.

The northern slopes are much quarried, into the main Cil yr Ychen beds of the Carboniferous Limestone, and Figure 46 shows how the quarry faces reveal fossiliferous localities in the succession. The long process of weathering is well illustrated, for few fossils are well-exposed yet in

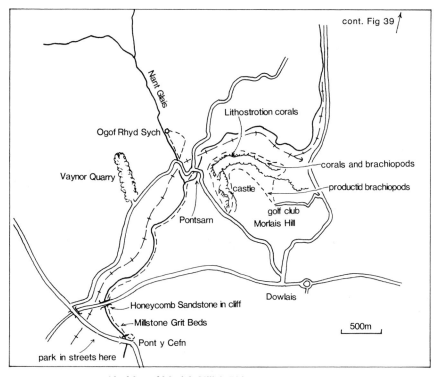

46   Map of Morlais Hill & Tâf Fechan gorge area.

comparison with those seen at natural outcrops. At 049099 there is a bed of the coral *Lithostrotion,* exposed 1m from the base of the 15m high quarry face, and further east along the quarries, corals and brachiopods can be seen.

Passing up to the castle and the hilltop beyond, the overlying Llandyfan Limestone outcrops, with the horizon of the Honeycomb Sandstone (see section on Tâf Fechan Gorge) revealed in boulders at 052094. Large productid brachiopods, *Productus hemisphericus* are seen in the south side of the small woodland at 054095 and rare trilobite remains (trilobites were close to extinction in Carboniferous Limestone times) are reported from 055094.

The southern slopes of the hill beyond the Club House and Castle Farm were quarried for the Basal Grits of the Millstone Grit. Morlais Castle is worth visiting on a clear day for the view northwards over Cwm Tâf Fechan, to the limestone dip-slope beyond, around Vaynor and Dan y bryn, Figure 47, and for the extensive panorama of the Old Red Sandstone country beyond, right up to the scarp summit of the Beacons at Corn Du, Pen y Fan and Cribin.

47   Looking north from Morlais Castle to the summits of the Brecon Beacons. The distant slopes are on the Old Red Sandstones, the nearer ones on the Carboniferous Limestone. The Tâf Fechan flows below the foreground slopes, too deeply incised to be visible in this view. (Photo: Glyn Davies)

Glais Valley and Ogof Rhyd Sych

From the Glais Bridge, 043098, a short walk can be made up the Nant y Glais to Ogof Rhyd Sych, the cave of the dry waterfall, more popularly known as the Beaver's Cave.

The brook follows the course of the Dowlais Fault and is a fine example of a fault-guided valley. It lies in the main Cil yr Ychen limestone at the Glais Bridge, but 300m upstream the Llanelly Formation outcrops, just north of the cave.

From the stile at Glais Bridge two routes are available. Either stick close to the east bank of the stream, through marshy spring-fed slopes, or climb northeast up the hillside to a path along the field boundaries above, eventually joining a double hedgebank of trees which border what is marked on the 1:25,000 map as an unfenced road. It is really only a grassy trackway and leads down to the river again at an old ford, close by the cave. On reaching that spot, the dry waterfall is seen immediately below, in solution worn limestones. The stream sinks into the river bed some 75m further up-valley, except in very wet winter weather when the falls become active again.

Large lumps of tufa have formed near the falls, sometimes exposed and broken by falling trees. More tufa can be seen forming from springs entering over the walls of the straight gorge-like cleft below the dry fall.

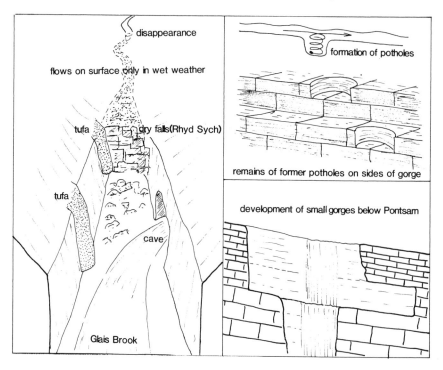

48   Some features of the Tâf Fechan gorge and the Glais Brook.

Descend the east side of the dry fall into the gully. At the bottom there is a good flow of water emerging from the east bank, as the Glais reappears from within the Beaver's Cave (Ogof Rhyd Sych).

Returning to Glais Bridge, the Nant y Glais shortly passes beneath a huge railway embankment built over it to carry the former railway line from Cefn Coed y Cymmer to Pontsticill, and then enters the Tâf Fechan below Pontsarn Bridge. Thus the examination of Ogof Rhyd Sych can easily form a short extension to the next walk to be described, the Tâf Fechan Gorge.

Tâf Fechan Gorge

This walk is most attractive if followed upstream, from urban to rural scenery. The route begins by the A470 bridge over the river at the southern end of Cefn Coed y Cymmer, Pont y Cefn, 037076. Cars can be parked off the A470 in the back streets NW of the bridge.

Cross to the east bank of the river via the small older bridge immediately north of Pont y Cefn. On the far bank turn right to gain the river bank directly beneath the road bridge, then proceed upstream.

49 Outcrops on the east side of the Tâf Fechan, immediately below the Heads of the Valleys Road bridge. The Honeycomb Sandstone outcrops at the top of the vertical face.

The pathway is an old tramroad and many stone chairs mark the route taken by limestone-laden wagons coming down from the quarries up valley to the Cyfarthfa Ironworks. However, we are not yet on the limestone outcrop and the rocks on the right are cross-bedded Millstone Grit. The fine waterfall a few metres up the path is a man-made feature, the overflow from the leat taking water to the lake in the grounds of Cyfarthfa Castle, formerly the home of the ironmaster Richard Crawshay. The river cliff here is in two sections, the lower face cut back to accommodate the tramroad, the upper one quarried out to build the leat.

Those with a head for heights can reach the rim of the leat, climbing up to it about 200m north of the waterfall, and then continue north along it. There is a big drop along the edge of the leat in places, so care is needed. The only advantage is a view of the junction of the Basal Grits of the Millstone Grit with the underlying Carboniferous Limestone. The boundary area is cavernous due to the solution of the upper surface of the limestones. Staying on the leat rim deprives the explorer of a good view of the next geological features upstream however, so it is best, and safer, to return to the lower path.

Proceed up-river to the point where the fine cantilever construction of the Heads of the Valleys road bridge soars high overhead. Several blocks of honeycombed beds lie about on the bank here. These are fallen blocks of the Honeycomb Sandstone, the important marker horizon which occurs at the S zone/D zone boundary in the Carboniferous Limestone over a wide area of the North Crop of the coalfield. Look up at the cliff-face which provides the eastern abutment for the bridge. The sandstone outcrops at the top of the vertical face.

Llandyfan Limestones {	Pale Grey oolitic limestone	3m
	Honeycomb Sandstone	1m ←Top of vertical face
	Pale grey oolitic limestone	10.5m

| Cil yr Ychen Limestone { | Dark grey limestone with brachiopods | 65m plus (down to river level) |

The vertical face is continued into the old ironworks limestone quarry up-river, and the horizon of the Honeycomb Sandstone can be followed visually along it. The overlying D zone limestones continue for a while, but shortly, to the east of Merthyr they are missing. They were eroded away from the eastern part of the South Wales coalfield structure soon after their own deposition, ie, before the deposition of the Millstone Grit.

Up-valley, all the limestone exposures for the rest of the walk as far as Pontsarn Bridge are in the main Cil yr Ychen limestones. The path crosses a stile into the old quarry floor, close by a dark grey limestone outcrop in the river. This was formerly the site of a bridge. The weir further upstream marks the intake point of the Cyfarthfa Castle leat.

Notice how the limestone beds in the river reveal the regional dip (here, across the river) to the S.SE. Thus this section of the Tâf Fechan is a strike valley. This has a notable effect on small tributaries. There are few on the southern bank, but on the north bank several emerge close to the level of the Tâf, coming down dip through the beds sloping towards the river on that side. Behind the main emerging tributary there is a dry valley, cut along the line of a fault which crosses the Tâf at this point. The fault can also be seen in an exposure on the south side of the Heads of the Valleys road at 037084.

Just beyond the next weir, a small affair of double elm boarding with a loose rock-fill, turn left down the bank and walk along a hidden rock ledge beneath overhangs of the uppermost limestone bed. Solution pot-holes and old waterfall plunge pools mark the bottom of this small, but very scenic, limestone gorge. Several 1m high waterfalls occur here. The lower limestone beds are more massive; the higher ones (including the overhanging bed) thinner and more flaggy. Tufa formation can be seen in the water-fed joints.

Notice that all the overhangs are on the southern, down-dip, bank – undercut, no doubt, as the stream flowed at that level and was continually thrown against that bank by the dip, Figure 48. The rocks dip 5 to 6° South along this part of the valley.

Back on the path above, 14m before an old iron gate-post there is a fine mass of tufa, building down over the limestone face on the right, petrifying the roots of mosses which cover its surface.

Cross a tributary stream and a second stile. Another limestone gorge follows and, again, descend into it and follow a ledge pathway upstream. This time it is possible to walk up and out through the head of the gorge. Notice the last stretch of the gorge upstream. It is cut very straight, along a major joint in the limestone which runs into the south bank eventually. Also near the top end, the edges of beds, now well above the river level, reveal the semi-circular remains of old pot-holes. Just above the gorge, the structures on the north bank are the sewage works for the village of Trefechan.

The stream coming in on the north bank just beyond comes from Vaynor Quarry. The quarry has silt traps to prevent the pollution of the stream by quarry debris. Vaynor Quarry also yields the purple fluorite described earlier at the New Tyle'r Bont (Baltic) quarry. The mineral must occur quite widely over the district at this particular level in the Carboniferous Limestone succession.

Further up, the tramroad pathway ends, and by the limestone-built retaining wall on the right, old moss-covered steps lead up the bank. No sign of rock chutes or other features remain to explain why the tramroad was built up as far as this spot. Could it have been to bring quarrymen up to work in the Morlais Hill quarries a short climb to the east?

The path beyond is more irregular. Where the gas pipeline crosses the river (orange marker) the slopes to the right appear to be of quarry waste, possibly from the construction of the former sanatorium on Pontsarn Hill, or

50 Gorge of the Tâf Fechan below Pontsarn, revealing a beautifully pot-holed bed in Carboniferous Limestones. The old Roman Road across the Beacons crossed the Tâf Fechan here. (Photo: Derek Packer)

perhaps, and as an explanation of the tramroad as well, was stone being brought down these slopes from the Morlais quarries?

A Millstone Grit millstone can be found further up the path, by a fenced enclosure which was the sewage works for the former sanatorium. The ruins of the old cornmill in which the stone was used, stand close by the river bank a few metres beyond. At this point another NW-SE trending fault crosses the

Tâf Fechan, the Dowlais Fault, and runs up the valley of the Glais Brook tributary opposite. High up on the right, ahead, the ruins of Morlais Castle crown a view of part of the extensive Morlais Quarries, which provided limestone for the Penydarren and Dowlais Ironworks.

Ford the river near the old mill and continue up the north bank into the fine limestone gorge crossed by Pont Sarn. As in the smaller examples seen earlier, the dip is across the river and the river is a strike stream. It is generally necessary to climb over the north bank to get a view of the Blue Pool, Pwll Glas, in the middle of the gorge. The pool is in fact never blue in colour, and the name may be a corruption of Pwll Glais, the Glais Pool.

Very large solution pot-holes occur in the Tâf just above and below Pont Sarn. The best view is from the edge of the north bank a few metres downstream of the bridge. Looking up the falls and pools at this narrowest point it is easy to see how the spot is such an ancient bridging point. The chasm could be easily spanned by a fallen tree. The old Roman road from Brecon crossed here, and then headed down the southern valleyside, through Gurnos towards Penydarren Park and thence to Gelligaer. From Pont Sarn, climb the hill northwards to the Aberglais Inn and it is then only a short walk down to Glais Bridge and the beginning of the itinerary for Ogof Rhyd Sych, page 74.

The Confluence

About 400m below the A470 bridge over the Tâf Fechan at Pont y Cefn, the two Tâf rivers meet, their confluence marking the southern limit of the districts we describe in this present volume. These two rivers form a superb open air laboratory, demonstrating so many geological features, and fortunately, the bulk of the area described here lies within the Brecon Beacons National Park. Anyone inclined to dismiss this park as "all Old Red Sandstone", less varied in its geology than other parks will, it is hoped, now see its considerable interest and usefulness.

References

Allen, J.R.L. The Devonian Rocks of Wales & the Welsh Borderline, in *The Upper Palaeozoic and Post Palaeozoic Rocks of Wales* (ed. T.R. Owen), University of Wales Press, 1974.

Hall, I.H.S., Taylor, K., Thomas, L.P. Stratigraphy of the upper Old Red Sandstone in South Breconshire. *Bulletin Geological Survey Great Britain,* No. 44, 1973.

Merthyr Teachers' Centre Group. *Merthyr Tydfil, A Valley Community.* D. Brown & Sons Ltd., Cowbridge, 1981.

Owen, T.R. The structure of the Neath Disturbance between Bryniau Gleision and Glynneath. *Quart. Jour. Geol. Soc. London,* 119, 1954, 333-365.

Pedler, F.J. *A History of the Hamlet of Gellideg.* Joseph Williams & Sons Ltd., Merthyr Tydfil, 1930.

Pringle, J. & George, T.N. *British Regional Geology, South Wales,* 2nd edn, H.M.S.O., 1948 and 3rd edn. (T.N. George only), 1970.

Robertson, T. & George, T.N. The Carboniferous Limestone of the North Crop of the South Wales Coalfield, *Proc. Geols. Assoc.* 40, 1929, 18-40.

Thomas, Trevor M. The Geomorphology of Brecknock, *Brycheiniog,* 5, 1959, 55-156.

Wright, V.P., Raven, M., Burchette, T.P. *Field Guide to the Lower Carboniferous Rocks near Abergavenny,* Department of Geology, Univeristy College, Cardiff, 1981.

Part Two: Social History

JACK EVANS

Early Travellers

The Tâf Fawr and Tâf Fechan rivers flow south south-east from the deeply dissected plateaux of the Brecon Beacons and form two deep valleys, along which the main roads have been made. These roughly parallel valleys are about ten miles long from the slopes of the Beacons to their junction just south of Cefn-Coed-y-Cymmer (Wooded ridge of the confluence). The moorland, much of it enclosed, and largely given over to sheep, mountain ponies and some conifers, is intersected by many deep, radiating valleys. It is the presence of so many valleys caused by the Tâf tributaries, so close to each other, that is responsible for the great and varied beauty of the scenery. The Tâf Fawr and Tâf Fechan rivers are now extensively utilised to feed reservoirs, but these have given an added dimension to the grandeur of the area.

It is always an intriguing, profitable and informative exercise to discover what other travellers, especially those of long ago, have said about this locality. We have always to keep in mind how intrepid these early travellers were, as Wales was largely unknown, the roads were rough, hotels were scarce and the available maps were poor. Furthermore, English visitors were virtually in a foreign country, as shown by these extracts from the Cefn Coed Schools Logbooks 1861-1956:-

1869 (April) Unless there is a change of Pupil Teachers the School cannot be worked efficiently. This School in particular requires *intelligent* teachers, those who are brought up by intelligent parents or friends, who as a rule speak English at home. The present staff *always* speak Welsh at home. Nearly all the scholars speak Welsh at home, too, consequently they want their teaching lessons explained, which the present P.T's are unable to do.

1872 (Sept) The children so Welshy and understand so little English, that there is considerable difficulty in making them discriminate the meaning of what they read.

1881 (Dec) Geography backward, the great difficulty being to get the children to *reproduce* their information in English.

1883 (May) Std.VII improving in composition – this is a most difficult subject to teach throughout the room – children speak so much Welsh at home.

It is salutary to compare the above sentiments, written by English Head-masters drafted into the schools by the local Ironmasters, with those in a very interesting and well written book by Wirt Sikes, the American Consul in Cardiff – "Rambles and Studies in Old South Wales 1881". "The Welsh population of Merthyr is gathered in large part from the mountains and wildish valleys hereabout, and includes some specimens of the race who (as the phrase goes) have no English, with a very large number of specimens who have but little and utter it brokenly.

Those of the lower class, who can read – and almost all Welshmen, however poor and primitive, can read, – generally read Welsh only; and in that respect, as indeed in most respects, are far in advance of Englishmen of the same state in life, who often can read nothing. To hear a poor and grimy Welshman, who looks as if he might not have a thought above bread and beer, talk about the poets and poetry of his native land, ancient and modern, is an experience which when first encountered, gives the stranger quite a shock of agreeable surprise."

Written accounts by the travellers do not appear until the 16th century. Before this time and stretching back for many centuries, what the inhabitants and tourists thought and observed must remain unrecorded. One would here have to turn to the historians who by their patient researching are able to piece together the story of man and the land in these distant times.

John Leland 1506-1552 was one of the first commentators with a range of observations. He was sent touring as the "Kings Antiquary" to visit libraries, monasteries, churches and colleges to make an inventory of objects of value scattered by the dissolution of the monasteries. In a general description of Breconshire he states:- "Breconshire is very mountainous, and in sum place very woody; nevertheless in the Valles fruteful of corn and especially of pastures, for the Walschmen yn tymes past, as they do almost yet, did study more to pasturage then tylling, as favorers of their consuete idilness". About Vaynor he mentions:- "Morelays Castelle standith in a good valley for corn and grasse, and is on the ripe of Morelais Brooke. The Castelle is in ruine and longith to the King.

Morelays riveret cummeth by north est out of Brekenocshire hilles toward High-Wenceland and so to Morelays's Castelle and about a myle lower in a paroche caullid Martyr it goith into the est ripe of Taue (Martyr Tedvil)".

Morlais Castle does not stand by the side of Morlais brook but is magnificently situated on a hill and not in a valley as stated by Leland. These topographical errors would probably be considered very minor details by him. The flash floods of the Tâf Fechan are now controlled by the reservoirs, but prior to these constructions how true the following must have been:-

"The water of Taphe cummith so down from woddy hilles, and often bringgith down such logges and trees, that the cuntery wer not able to make up the bridges if they were stone they should be so often broken".

Holinshed ("Chronicles of England, Scotland and Ireland" 2 vols 1578) was another of the early travellers.

"Certes the Taff is the greatest river in all Glamorganshire called by Ptolemy "Rhatostathybius" as I gesse. It riseth in Breconshire among the woodie hills from two heads whereof one is the Monuchdennie (Beacons) and the other west of that mountaine of which the first is called Taffe Vawre, (Tâf Fawr), the other Taffe Vehan (Tâf Fechan) which goeth by Capel Lan Vehan (Capel Tâf Fechan) Veynor and Morlais, the other to Capel Nantee (Nantddu) and adjoining at S.W. beneath Morlais Castle they go by Martyr Tidvil towards Llanabor (Llanvabon) but by the way it taketh in from the North West a brooke called Cunnon (Cynon) which cometh out of Brecknockshire by Aberdare and afterwards the Rodnei (Rhondda) coming out of the same quarter but not out of the same shire".

The most noteworthy traveller into our area in the eighteenth century was *Daniel Defoe, ("Tour through the whole of Britain" 1724-26)* author of 'Robinson Crusoe'. He travelled from Breconshire along the Tâf Fawr into Glamorganshire. Defoe had no feeling for wild places and positively disliked rocks and precipices.

"We began with Brecknock, being willing to see the highest of the mountains which are said to be hereabouts; and indeed, except I still had an idea of the height of the Alps, I should have been surprised at the sight of these hills. We were saluted with Monuchdenny-Hill (Beacons) on our left, and the Black Mountain on the right and all a ridge of horrid rocks and precipices between, over which, if we had not had trusty guides we should never have found our way, and indeed we began to repent our curiosity, as not having met with anything worth the trouble; and a country looking so full of horror, that we thought to have given over the enterprise and have left Wales out of our circuit. But after a day and a night conversing thus with rocks and mountains, our guide brought us down into a most agreeable vale, opening to the south and a pleasant river running through it, called the Taaffe; and following the course of this river, we came in the evening to the ancient city of Llandaff, and Caerdiff standing almost together".

Another traveller *G.W. Manby ("An Historic and Picturesque Guide through the counties of Monmouth, Glamorgan and Brecknock — 1802")* gives a very rambling and verbose account of a journey in the opposite direction from Merthyr to Brecon through the Tâf Fawr Valley. It also identifies the language difficulties. ". . .the atmosphere became in sable tint and I was soon driven by the pitiless storm to seek shelter at Half Way House, a very humble pile indeed, and appearing to be raised for the residence of undisturbed solitude; but the study to please made me forget everything beyond common comforts were superfluous; neither the good old woman nor her handmaid could speak English, nor I the dialect of their country, however, with various actions of dumb show I had all my wants supplied; on the storm being appeased, and the face of heaven resuming its

83

wanted serenity, pursued my journey; the country now became poor in trees and the steep bare mountains were spotted with sheep picking a scanty subsistence; the sides of this range of lofty hills were grooved by the power of winter torrents whose numerous tributary streams account for the hasty rise of the river; here passing over a small bridge I took leave of the river which had been my companion for upwards of forty miles, no longer of consequence to set limits to my admiration, but dwindled into a trifling brook only a few feet wide and retiring to the right, is lost among the mountains where it reaches its origin''.

But we should not be too critical of some of these early travellers because their powers of walking would put most of us to shame.

Benjamin Heath Malkin (1769-1842) — Professor of History at London University, who eventually retired to Cowbridge, wrote *"The Scenery, Antiquities and Biography of South Wales"* which was compiled from material collected during two excursions in the year 1803.

"From the Castle near Gelly Vallog (Morlais Castle) therefore I now pursue the old road to Brecon over the mountains, when the dingle on the left, through which runs Neath Vechan (Tâf Fechan) river is deep, wild and precipitous. The rough and stony horse-path, for the new turnpike road winds round the bases of the mountains to the west, is carried over to the top of the precipice and affords successively a complete view of the circling dell, through which the eastern branch of the Neath river (Tâf Fechan) runs, dividing Brecknockshire from Glamorganshire in its course. The winding down the hill to the waterside is picturesque — and verdant and brings the traveller to Pont Stickel (Pontsticill), a bridge of one arch, crossing Neath Vechan river, after which the mountains to be climbed on the left and the scenery of the dingle on the right become less verdant. The two peaks of Mounchdeny Mountain (The Beacons) now present themselves in a different direction. They may almost be said to personify ubiquity. The one is more pointed than the other; but both, enveloped in clouds, communicate a grandeur to the prospect, which compensates in great measure for its poverty and want of beauty. A green lane, enclosed with overhanging hedges, and inclining to the right, leads again to the riverside, which is here quiet, shallow and translucent, crossed by a bridge of one long narrow trunk, without railing. There is some wood about the banks. Chapel Glyncollwm is near the spot, not otherwise observable than as affording an evidence to the senses, that though the abodes of men do not present themselves to the eye, there are occupiers of these unfrequented sheep-walks, and those occupiers are civilized. After passing Chapel Glyncollwm, the path soon leads to the foot of Mounchdenny Mountain, which has long appeared immediately in front, and now presents a lengthy, laborious and dreary ascent. A stone bridge is thrown across Neath Vechan, the last effort of human art to tame and render commodious the passage of the mountain, when this uncommercial track afforded the only communication between Merthyr Tydfil and Brecknock''.

It is noticeable that many of the early travellers, and, indeed, the early cartographers were not unduly worried about the correct spelling of place names, or in getting some of the names completely wrong.

Another great pedestrian and an outstanding local historian was *Theophilus Jones 1759-1812* who wrote the comprehensive *"History of Breconshire 1809"*. He was the son of the vicar of Llangammarch, trained as a solicitor, and became the Deputy Registrar to the Archdeaconship. This very talented man had this to say about one of his short walks − "From the village of Coed-y-Cymmer adjoining the turnpike road to, and at the distance of two miles from Merthyr, we proceed up along the banks of the lesser Tâf over Coed-y-Cymmer, a barren stony common; but on the approach to the church several picturesque dells cross the road. Through one of them runs the sheltered rivulet of the Glais (from its banks being covered with wood), which empties itself into the Tâf, but these dingles are not formed for the traveller; the ascents and descents are frequently so abrupt and the road so bad that we recommend the man of weak nerves, however fond he may be of landscape, not to indulge in his favourite study at the risk of his neck. If, however, he is determined to try the experiment, even on foot, he will have an admirable opportunity of doing so by crossing the river Tâf at a little distance below the church, over a tremendous wooden bridge called Pont Sarn, thrown from rock to rock, of the height of about thirty or forty feet from the water. At a little above is a cavern called Ogof Rhyd Sych, or Dryford Cavern; this hollow in the lime rock receives a spring from above, which sinks into the ground and then enters the cave, from whence it issues in a small rill in times of flood when it flows over it and forms a cascade. Crossing the hill from thence westwards, all is barrenness till we come to the Vale of Tâf-fawr, where the soil is remarkably favourable to the production of trefoil, insomuch that if a field is sown with corn one year and left to rest the next, a verdure spontaneously arises, the meillionen or Dutch clover appears abundantly, and may be even mowed with profit; but such is the influx of mouths to Merthyr, that immediate interest and the increased demand for bread are consulted, and the plough continually interrupts and counteracts the inclination of nature".

It is interesting to compare the description of the Pontsarn Bridge given here with the dramatic portraiture given by *T.E. Clark in "A Guide to Merthyr Tydfil and the Travellers Companion 1848"*. "At the bottom of a vast mass of limestone and on the West side of Castell Morlais or Morley's Castle is the cataract of Pontysarn on the lesser Tâf River. The bridge is erected over two rocks of equal height having no more than eighteen feet between. When a person stands on the bridge and looks down the appearance is sufficient to inspire awe and unnerve the spectator because the river can hardly be seen between the deep cliffs, concealing itself as it were from public gaze and telling of its presence only by the thunder of its falls. The bridge is a wooden structure nine feet in width. It was formerly much narrower, consisting only of a few planks".

Nowadays, with wide, safe, tarmacadam roads, we can be faintly amused by this excerpt relating to Cwmtaf in *"Vaynor, its History and Guide" by J.E. Jenkins, 1897.* "Craig y Darren Vawr is 1,443 feet above sea level, the unapproachable home of the eagle, the hawk, the kite and the raven. The Craig overhangs as it were the high road that leads from Brecon to Coed-cymmer. This is the place where one of the King's Judges whilst being conveyed from Brecon to the Cardiff Assize seventy years ago (1827) said to his valet, "If God will allow me to go safe through this pass today, I will never come this way again".

It was here also, during the stirring times of the Merthyr Riots (1831) that the people collected huge boulders along the top of Darren Fawr, and rolled them down on Companies of soldiers sent from Brecon to quell the riots in Merthyr. This tactic delayed the red-coats for a very long time and only by crossing the valley to the other side did they finally reach their destination.

Perhaps the most famous person to have visited and written about our area is that great naturalist Alfred Russell Wallace who, with Charles Darwin (Joint Paper read at the Linnean Society on July 1st 1858:- "On the tendencies of species to Form Varieties; and on the Perpetuation of Varieties and Species by Natural means of Selection") had such a dramatic impact and influence on future biological thinking. It was in the Neath Valley, where with his brother, he resided for some years, surveying land for the developing railway companies, that he first taught himself botany when he purchased in 1841 a shilling paper-covered book on flora published by the Society for the Diffusion of Useful Knowledge.

In 'My Life' he describes a walk (1846) with his brother from Neath to Brecon. "The next morning early we proceeded up the valley from Ystrad-fellte to the highest farm on the Dringarth, then struck across the mountain to the road from Hirwaun to Brecon which we followed to the bridge over the Taff, and then turned off towards the Beacons, the weather being perfect. It was a delightful walk, on a gradual slope of fifteen hundred feet in a mile and a half, with a little steeper bit at the end, and the small over-hanging cap of peat at the summit. I searched over it for beetles, which were, however, very scarce, and we then walked along the ridge to the second and higher triangular summit, peeped with nervous dread on my part over the almost perpendicular precipice towards Brecon, noted the exact correspond-ence in slope of the two peat summits, and then back to the ridge and a little way down the southern slope to where a tiny spring trickles out – the highest source of the river Taff – and there lying on the soft mountain turf, enjoyed our lunch and the distant view over valley and mountain to the faint haze of the Bristol Channel. We then returned to the western summit, took a final view of the grand panorama around us, and bade farewell to the beautiful mountain, the summit of which neither of us visited again, though I have since been very near it".

As more people travelled around Wales, there was a demand to know what places to visit, how best to get there, and where to stay. This gave rise to the

'Guide' type of book such as Rev. T. Rees's 'Description of South Wales 1813', Samuel Lewis's 'Topographical Dictionary of Wales 1833' and the best of them all Emilius Nicholson's 'Cambrian Travellers' Guide 1840'. They were all surprisingly comprehensive and for the travellers of the time gave a very wide range of information, such as the following in the latter book which gives a route from Merthyr Tydfil to Brecon. "The new Turnpike-Road to Merthyr Tydfil presents a succession of varied and interesting scenery. The distances are Cefn-Coed-Cymmer 2¼m; Garawen 2¼m; cross Carr Brook 1m; cross the Llyseuog river 1m; Capel-nant-du ½m; cross Nant-du Brook 1½m. The last of these tributary streams to the Taff Fawr, is called Crew 1½m; Bryndu 2m; cross the Tarell river 4m; Brecon 4m."

And how this must have titillated the senses of the fishing fraternity! "Angling Stations – Glyn Conan, on the Taff, 7½m; salmon, sewin and trout. The vicinity of Merthyr Tydfil has greatly contributed to render certain portions of the romantic stream of the Taff unworthy of the angler's attention".

And so we have had vivid descriptions by tourists and historians, some only a century ago, of struggles over high mountains and craggy rocks, of battling through deep valleys on rough roads, and of the risk to life and limb negotiating deep and swift rivers. They have written of the joys to be experienced and the beauties to be admired.

It seems barely credible that in such a short space of time since then, one can meet on the peaks of the Beacons, present day tourists who started on their journey from London and Birmingham only a few hours earlier. There is now no pause in progress and development and often 'no time to stand and stare', as was the wont of the earlier travellers.

The Early Hunter-Gatherers and Farmers

A glance at the Ordnance Survey Map south of the Beacons shows the great number of cairns marked on the uplands adjoining the Tâf Fechan and Tâf Fawr valleys. This manifests the presence of prehistoric man in the area, and from excavations of various sites and discoveries of several implements, prehistoric man is shown to have occupied these uplands from as early as 6000 B.C. (Mesolithic – the Middle Stone Age). These bleak and sometimes barren moorlands may now strike you as a very unfriendly, lonely and often sodden place in which to have settled. But in Mesolithic, Neolithic (New Stone Age c 3000-1800 B.C.) and Bronze Age times (c 1800-400 B.C.) the climate was much warmer and drier than today's and must have been very pleasant habitats for man, even in winter. This is well demonstrated by Sian Bird (Thesis University College of Wales 1974-1975) who did a comprehensive Pollen Analysis in the Sychbant Valley (OS 985096) a bleak and well-watered moorland with large areas of blanket bog. From pollen diagrams which were produced she provided evidence that oak, birch, alder and lime formed a canopy of open woodland, supporting an understorey of hazel and willow, whilst various grasses, heathers, rose species and composite flowers occupied the open spaces on the valley slopes. In an area such as this, apart from the hunting which would have taken place, cultivation of the land was also possible, and by about 2500 B.C. efficient mixed farming must have been practised over much of our upland regions. This again is borne out by the pollen-analyses which when tabulated showed the decreasing tree curves and increasing herb counts in different localities, suggesting the various phases of tree clearance by the early farmers. In one particular area a recovery in woody vegetation takes place to be followed by a clearance phase again in which cultivation is demonstrated by the presence of Cornflower pollen (centaurea cyanus) and weed species such as plantain (Plantago), thistles, (Cirsium), sorrel (Rumex) and nettle (Urtica).

These earlier farmers would have occupied themselves with making leather clothing, since at this period there is no evidence of spinning and

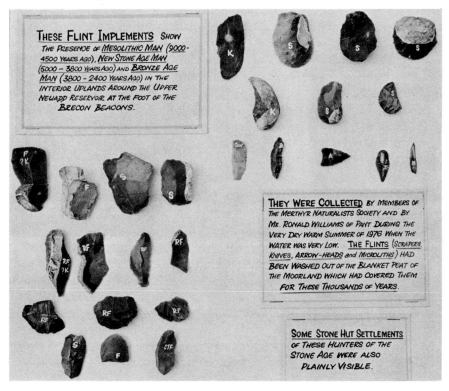

THESE FLINT IMPLEMENTS SHOW THE PRESENCE OF MESOLITHIC MAN (9000-4500 YEARS AGO), NEW STONE AGE MAN (5000 – 3800 YEARS AGO) AND BRONZE AGE MAN (3800 - 2400 YEARS AGO) IN THE INTERIOR UPLANDS AROUND THE UPPER NEUADD RESERVOIR AT THE FOOT OF THE BRECON BEACONS.

THEY WERE COLLECTED BY MEMBERS OF THE MERTHYR NATURALISTS SOCIETY AND BY MR. RONALD WILLIAMS OF PANT DURING THE VERY DRY WARM SUMMER OF 1976 WHEN THE WATER WAS VERY LOW. THE FLINTS (SCRAPERS, KNIVES, ARROW-HEADS and MICROLITHS) HAD BEEN WASHED OUT OF THE BLANKET PEAT OF THE MOORLAND WHICH HAD COVERED THEM FOR THESE THOUSANDS OF YEARS.

SOME STONE HUT SETTLEMENTS OF THESE HUNTERS OF THE STONE AGE WERE ALSO PLAINLY VISIBLE.

51   Key to Tool Types

A — Arrowhead	M — Microlith
B — Blade	S — Scraper
F — Flake	CTF — Core Trimming Flake
K — Knife	RTF — Re-touched Flake

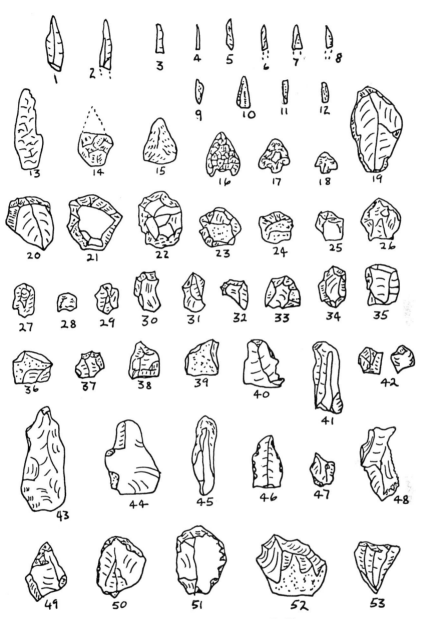

52 Flint assemblage found at Pant Sychbant.

Key to Flints

Flint Number	Implement			
1-12	Microliths	44	Single blow graver	47	Notched blade of chert
13-18	Arrowheads	45	Plano—convex knife	48	Serrated flake
19-42	Scrapers	46	Blade trimmed to a	49	Flake
43	Javelin point		point	50-53	Scrapers

weaving. They used flint tools for scraping the skins and probably made combs from bones and antlers, for removing the animal hair. Mr. T.W. Burke of Cardiff did indeed show that these activities of the Mesolithic people and later occupations, were much in evidence. He excavated a flint bearing layer near the head of Pant Sychbant (OS 995098) and found a number of microliths together with Neolithic and Bronze Age flints and fragments of pottery. Microliths are very small flint flakes that were used for mounting as part of a composite tool e.g. arrow heads or harpoon barbs. Further to the west, on the moorlands of the Rhondda Valley, Mr. Shôn Price, following the ploughing of tracks through the peat by the Forestry Commission discovered a great number of these microliths together with the 'cores' of flints from which they were made. The whole fascinating collection of flints discovered by Mr. Price is in the National Museum of Wales, Cardiff. Another amateur archaeologist, Mr. P.M. Tomsett whilst studying the ploughed furrows made by forestry machines in the Sychbant Valley discovered a similar deposit of flints mainly of Neolithic and Bronze Age character. Mr. Tomsett also discovered the butt of a partially polished Neolithic axe head at the old Cefn-y-Maes Farm (OS 997117) which proved on analysis by Professor F.W. Shotton of Birmingham, to have come from the flint factories near Craig Llwyd, Penmaenmawr.

Yet another of the amateur archaeologists, Mr. Derek Webley has undertaken several excavations in the Upper Tâf areas resulting in important contributions to the pre-history of Brecknock. He explored one of the 'Cairn Cemeteries' on Cefn Cilsanws, about one mile from the village of Cefn Coed (OS 025099), and discovered what was thought to be the first example of 'Secondary Neolithic' hut to be recorded in Wales (Bulletin of the Board of Celtic Studies XVIII (1958)). There was a complex pattern of stake holes which were interpreted to form a flimsy bee-hive hut about 12ft long by 7½ft wide. Some fragments of Neolithic pottery were also found. Mr. Andrew Robertson ("Merthyr Tydfil – A Valley Community" – published 1981) disagrees with this interpretation and considers that the stake holes represent a ritual structure belonging to the early Bronze Age and probably associated with the Bronze Age Cairn that covered it. Be that as it may, there are many cairns in the vicinity of this particular example, and with the possibility of more precise and accurate dating methods in the future, the true picture may yet unfold.

The very warm summer of 1976 led to the discovery of another large collection of Mesolithic, Neolithic and Bronze Age flints. The Upper Neuadd reservoir became dry and the banks of the river which had been submerged for more than a hundred years were now exposed. The blanket of peat which had covered the slopes had eroded away, and the fishermen members of the Merthyr Naturalists' Society began reporting the discovery of various flints. This led to a systematic search by the Society and many microliths, scrapers, arrowheads (including a superb barb-and-tang specimen) and knife blades were collected and eventually analysed by the archaeological department of the National Museum, Cardiff. As recently as 1981, a flint knife was found further south, on the west bank of the Tâf Fechan reservoir close to the dam.

The lives of these early farmers were not limited to the material preoccupation of hunting, keeping cattle and growing food. Added to the rhythm of the seasons and the cattle round-up there would be the matter of disposing and honouring the dead, which was the cause of deep concern for many primitive communities, as indeed it is for all communities today.

It was about 2000 B.C. that a group of people of European origin began infiltrating into the uplands, who, as well as being pastoralists had discovered how to make Bronze (an alloy of Copper and Tin), and thus the invasion became known as the Bronze Age. They were called the Beaker Folk from the kind of distinctive pottery they placed with their interred dead. They also practised cremation, the remains being placed in a Cinerary Urn and covered with a round cairn, many of which are still to be seen in our upland areas. Excavations of many of these had taken place, some scientifically, but unfortunately over the years a great number have been wantonly pillaged and destroyed.

Some good examples of urns were found at Abercar Farm in Cwmtaf (now submerged under Llwyn-On Reservoir) in 1859, when the farmer, a Mr. Henry Thomas, while working in the fields found a Cinerary Urn and a Pygmy Cup, the former covering the cremated remains of a body. The Pygmy Cup, the smaller of the two, contained a small quantity of burnt oak and ash, probably connected in some way with the burial ceremony. Both these pots are in the Museum of the Royal Institution of South Wales, Swansea.

Mr. Derek Webley has excavated (1958-59) two early Bronze Age burial sites fairly close to each other at Twyn Bryn Glas, between Cwmtaf and Penderyn (OS 987117) and at Nantmaden Farm on the western side of the Cwm Cadlan Road between Cwmtaf and Penderyn (OS 971106). The former was a complicated structure in which there had been a series of burials, the primary burials showing signs of disturbance. Fragments of various beakers were found together with a plain globular Pygmy Cup. The latter cairn is very impressive, with a large standing stone in the middle and a ring of large boulders forming the circular boundary. This cairn had been irresponsibly interfered with in the past, and the ritual pit covered by a slab was empty. Fragments of Cinerary Urns and pieces of Beakers were found.

A beaker was also found in a stone cist (a grave lined with stone slabs) at Cwmcar Farm, Dolygaer, together with some burnt bones and a flint barb-and-tang arrow head. The well-made brick-red beaker has been described and recorded by Sir Mortimer Wheeler, but unfortunately the whereabouts of the finds are now unknown.

Not many bronze objects have been found in our area as this metal would have been relatively scarce, particularly at the beginning of the Bronze Age, and flint was still the principal material used in the manufacture of

53   Ring Cairn on Cilsanws mountain. 026 124.   *Jack Evans*

implements. During the construction of the Llwyn-On reservoir a very fine
bronze palstave – a type of axe – was discovered and dated to circa 1000
B.C. This is now in the National Museum, Cardiff. Another good example,
this time of a bronze dagger of the Early Bronze Age, was found in one of the
round cairns on Cilsanws in 1908 and presented to the Cyfarthfa Museum,
Merthyr, where it may now be seen. But not far away at Llyn Fawr, near
Hirwaun (036 915) at the head of the Rhondda Fawr Valley was found the
most important hoard of late Bronze objects (circa 600 B.C.) in the whole of
Britain. These are kept in the National Museum, Cardiff. Amongst the
hoard were parts of an iron sword, a spear head and a sickle which would
mark the end of the Bronze Age, and the beginning of the Iron Age. The two
cultures would obviously have co-existed and merged for a long period and
definite dates assigned to them are only used for convenience.

During the Iron Age from about the 6th century B.C. onwards settlement
patterns became more varied, some being small homesteads with a small
number of unenclosed hut settlements while others would be larger communities associated with the hill forts defended by a palisade or a rampart and
ditch. Few have been found in our area, and of these one is a site at Morlais
Castle, built upon and largely destroyed by the Normans, and the other a hill
slope enclosure at Dolygaer (059 148) which has not been excavated. But
close to our area at Gwersyll on Mynydd Merthyr (024 042) is a site of the
defended kind where the semi-circular rampart (which suggests the site was
vacated before being completed) can be plainly seen, whilst not far away at
Buarth Maen (012 053) on the Mynydd Aberdâr ridge is quite an impressive

unenclosed hut group. The site consists of a number of variably placed round huts joined by partly round enclosure walls, some quite large, of up to 60m across. The huts range from about 2½ metres up to about 6 metres in diameter. Outside the enclosure and to the west is a fairly large cairn.

Another settlement, fairly similar to Buarth Maen, but not quite so extensive, is to be found at Mynydd Cefn-y-Gyngon about a mile and a half south of Hirwaun and 200 yards north of the source of Nant Melyn (957034).

We can thus assume a continuity of life in our area, backwards from the hill forts and the open hut enclosures, through the Bronze Age to the Stone Age. The old idea of migrations and exchanges of whole populations must be forsaken for the gradual implementation of new ideas and the slow integration of different cultures. Groups of men ceased to live as bands of hunters but began to cultivate the land with flint, and later on, metal implements. They domesticated animals, made clay containers and developed many other techniques.

It would be completely wrong to think of these people as 'primitive'. They had highly developed and strongly distinctive cultures with a high level of technical skill and artistic imagination. The great number of burial sites scattered around our area suggests a rich cultural life, and the fact that they left behind only sparse fragments of flint and metal is accounted for by the fact that objects made of wood, leather, bark or even bone would be unlikely to survive.

As archaeologists are very thin on the ground there are many opportunities for the enthusiastic amateur to discover and record other pre-history sites around the Tâf river uplands and valleys. New and interesting facts about our early ancestors are waiting to be revealed by patient excavating.

Glimpses of Roman and Norman Presence

During the Roman occupation of Wales, their road from the coastal fort at Cardiff to Y Gaer at Brecon, passed through the Tâf Fechan Valley. Parts of it can still be found crossing the summit of the Fochrhiw mountain, from the fort at Gelligaer from whence it probably proceeded to the fort at Penydarren in Merthyr. It can then be traced at the Gurnos Farm, when it takes a course over the Tâf Fechan at Pontsarn Bridge (Pont-sarn-hir – The bridge of the long paved road) and continues to the Glais brook. It then follows the eastern side of the Glais for a short way, passes behind Penrhiwglais farm, where traces of the road can still be seen, and crosses the main road by Vaynor Cottage. There are no traces of the road from here to the Church, but a very good portion is clearly discernible about three hundred yards from the Church Tavern, as the road makes its way to Pen-yr-adwy, Pontsticill Another section can be found at the Ynys Farm in Pontsticill close to where it is submerged by the Tâf Fechan reservoir. The road can be clearly seen again from the Lower Neuadd reservoir as it makes its way to the east of the Cribin peak and through the "Gap".

The Roman roads were frequently set up along the ridgeways whose use went back into prehistoric times and also along other routes used by Silurian tribes. It is practically certain that they continued to be used until at least the early part of the 7th century. Dr. Nash Williams (late Keeper of Department of Archaeology, National Museum of Wales) for instance, in a presidential address to the Cardiff Naturalists' Society in 1947 demonstrated that the pattern of Ogham stones indicates a route along the old Roman Road from Llandovery to Y Gaer, Brecon. These Ogham stones are very interesting. With the departure of the Roman armies from Britain in the late 4th century there was a growth of trade towards the Irish Sea and a furthering of cultural connections between the Celtic peoples. There could well have been an actual Irish settlement in the late Roman period and this is borne out by place

54   Ogham Stone near Cwar yr Ystrad, Pontsticill.   *Jack Evans*

names in the area. On the Ordnance Map on Mynydd Aberdâr is Bryn-y-Gwyddel (The Irishman's Hill) (OS 007072) and at a point a little south of this is Bedd-y-Gwyddel (The Irishman's Grave). This is in the form of a large mound cross about twenty-two yards in length. Tudvyl, the daughter of Brychan Brycheiniog, of Irish extraction and the ruler of Breconshire and a small principality in South Wales during the 5th century, is commemorated in the name of Merthyr Tydfil. From one of Tudvyl's sisters, Sanos, we get Cilsanws, at the foot of which nestles Cefn-Coed-y-Cymmer.

This occupation is also demonstrated by rough stone pillars and slabs bearing contemporary inscriptions. Many of these, commonly found in what was the county of Breconshire, bear an inscription in the Irish script known as Ogham. This was a remarkable kind of alphabet which probably originated in Ireland during Pagan times. It consists of short lines or scores numbering from one to five corresponding to the five fingers of the hand, and arranged in different ways with regard to a central stem line.

In the Cyfarthfa Museum, Merthyr Tydfil, in the recess opposite the 'Welsh Room' is a stone of Old Red Sandstone on which is inscribed these Ogham characters and a cross, dated 5th or 6th century. It was found originally at Penllwyneinon Farm, Ystradfellte, but was later removed to Fedw Hir Farm, Llwydcoed.

The Ogham Characters on the Cyfarthfa Stone

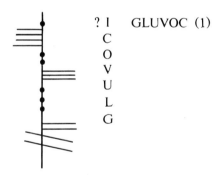

? I   GLUVOC (1)
C
O
V
U
L
G

By all accounts these stones were once common in our area, but most have now disappeared. Nevertheless, one can still be seen, standing in glorious isolation at the headwaters of Nant Criban and to the west of Cwar yr Ystrad (OS 074 132). The best approach to this site is along a footpath marked on the Ordnance Map and which commences about 200 yards south of the Tâf Fechan Reservoir dam.

Little or no improvement had been made to the roads built by the Romans until the beginning of the last century. It can be well understood why these primitive conditions persisted, firstly because people had no need for good roads as they travelled on their own two feet or on horseback, and, secondly, the villagers were expected to maintain the roads without being re-imbursed. Since the 16th century, people were required by law to give six days each year towards repairing the roads, when they were expected to even supply tools, horses and carts. Thus the road from Cefn Coed-y-Cymmer to Pontsticill made the steep ascent of the hill at the Glais Bridge (over the existing stile and on the Roman Road) to the Pen-rhiw'r-glais Farm, and then made the descent on the other side. It was not until 1832 that the parishioners decided this route was exceedingly difficult and burdensome and made arrangements to provide a better road, which now loops from the Glais to Vaynor Cottage.

The growth of Merthyr as the country's largest industrial centre, and its proximity to Brecon with its rich agricultural land, made it imperative that a good road be constructed between the two towns. Certain farmers and manufacturers invested their money in the new Turnpike roads, with interest to be paid from the tolls extracted from the travellers on the roads. This scheme resulted in new roads being built and existing roads improved.

The tolls paid, with increases over the years, were as follows:- carriages – 3d a horse; packhorse or riding horse – 1d; cattle 10d a score; sheep, calves, pigs, lambs – 5d a score. The toll, by law, could only be levied once a day, (this was later changed to travellers being allowed only three times in 24 hours) and no payment was paid on any vehicle carrying manure, lime, hay or corn from one part of a farm to another, nor was payment made on any animals moved in the same way.

In the three years after 1840 when harvests were poor due to long, cold and wet spells, the farmers in their poverty rebelled against paying tolls and

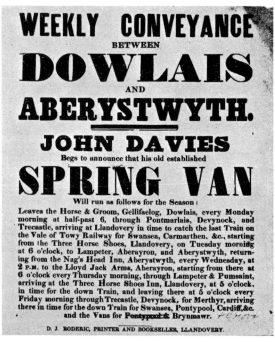

55   A Coach which had its Booking Office and starting place at the Horse and Groom, Gellifaelog, Dowlais.

started the Rebecca Riots (so called, because the rioters wore women's clothing when they attacked the gates). As a consequence of this long, bitter and acrimonious struggle, the tolls were lowered and eventually Parliament accepted responsibility for the roads.

The Turnpike main road from Merthyr to Brecon through the Tâf Fawr valley was finished as far as the Storey Arms in 1814, with a Toll Gate at the Darren (see map, page 107). The road was completed as far as Brecon in 1831, being diverted from the east side of the valley to the west. The old road from the Storey Arms to Brecon can still be seen, and it affords a very pleasant walk away from the traffic on the present A470.

With the improvement in the roads, long-distance public transport using Stage Coaches, became possible. They travelled throughout the year in all weathers, running to a fairly tight schedule, and one can well imagine the rigours and discomforts experienced by the passengers on cold and wintry days, particularly those who had booked outside seats. Typical fares would be those as advertised by a Light Post Coach in 1826, leaving the Castle Inn,

Protection against Broken Limbs.

T̶HE Public are respectfully informed, that the new and elegant STAGE CARRIAGE,

THE IMPERIAL,

The only Vehicle of the kind in the Principality, which runs between *Swansea, Neath, Merthyr,* and *Brecon,* will, in future, run to the CASTLE-INN, at BRECON, where it has formed a connexion with the Hereford, Worcester, Wolverhampton and Birmingham Coaches.

The IMPERIAL starts from the Wheat Sheaf Inn, Swansea, at a quarter before eight every Tuesday, Thursday, and Saturday morning; from the Bush Inn, Merthyr, for Brecon, at two in the afternoon, where it arrives about five the same evening.

Leaves the Castle-Inn, Brecon, on its return, at seven every Wednesday, Friday, and Sunday morning—Merthyr at ten—and arrives at Swansea about four that evening.

This Conveyance arrives at and leaves Brecon so as also to suit the arrival and departure of the Mail Coaches to Llandovery, Llandilo, Carmarthen, Abergavenny, Monmouth, Gloucester; and the Dart to and from Builth, Llandrindod, Newtown, Welshpool, &c. &c.

☞ The Proprietors beg leave to appeal to those Ladies and Gentlemen who have already travelled by the Imperial, as to the very *superior comfort,* particularly *in wet weather,* and the *security* it affords (from its peculiarly sale construction) against breaking down or up-setting from being overloaded ; which advantages, no other *Stage* Conveyance on the same line of road can possibly offer.

56 Safe travelling was promised by the Imperial which had one of the booking offices and starting places at the Bush Inn, Merthyr.

Merthyr Tydfil every morning at 6 a.m. for Bristol, through Abergavenny.

Fare — Inside, One Pound; Outside, twelve shillings.

Heavy luggage and parcels — 1d per pound;

Small parcels — 2s 2d each.

This was a considerable sum of money in those days when beer was no more than one penny a pint and the majority of workmen would have earned a sum far less than 20s a week. A miner, for instance, would have earned about 12s to 15s a week for working twelve to thirteen hours per day, out of which he would have paid 2s per week for rent and about the same per week for coal. He would possibly keep a wife and five small children on this wage. Even this small sum could be three to four times the wages of a rural worker, which accounted for the influx of country folk to the industrial centre of Merthyr Tydfil.

The *Imperial*, one of the Companies which appeared in 1827, ran a service between Swansea and Brecon via Neath, Merthyr and through the Tâf Fawr valley, connecting with coaches to Llandovery, Carmarthen, Abergavenny, Monmouth and Gloucester.

A large volume 'Paterson's Roads' published in 1822 gave interesting descriptions of towns and villages through which the coaches passed, and the entry for the route Aberystwyth to Cardiff through Builth, Brecon and Merthyr Tydfil makes engaging reading.

A visual reminder of the occupation of our area by the Normans is at the beginning of the parish road near Vaynor House leading to Vaynor Church. Immediately on the right is a large mound and to the west on the other side of the valley are the Morlais Quarries surmounted by what has the shape of an extinct volcano — Morlais Castle. It is now in almost complete ruin, only the moat, the outline of the walls and grass-covered debris remaining. The crypt, nevertheless, is still intact, and demonstrates the sturdy nature of Norman structures. There are extensive panoramic views from the site, which is typical of an Iron-Age hill fort, the earlier occupier of this limestone scarp.

The castle was built about the year 1270 by Gilbert de Clare, Earl of Gloucester and Lord of Glamorgan, but presumably was not completed, although it was occasionally occupied by troops. Another powerful Marcher Lord of this period was Humphrey de Bohun, Earl of Hereford and Lord of Brecknock who objected to the building of the castle on what he considered was his land. The dispute became very bitter, the Glamorganshire men making frequent incursions into Breconshire from the castle, plundering wherever they marched, burning the churches and stealing the cattle. De Bohun retaliated and eventually a pitched battle between the two forces took place at Maes-y-Faenor, close to the present crossroads between Pontsarn and Pontsticill.

ABERYSTWITH TO CARDIFF, THROUGH BUALT, BRECON, AND MERTHYR TYDVIL.

THE BRIDGEWATER ARMS, near, Pont-y-Prydd, or New Bridge. The appearance of this elegant structure which stretches over the river Taf, and rises from its steep banks like a rainbow, is exceedingly beautiful and picturesque from every point of view in which it can be seen. It consists of a single arch 140 feet in the chord, and 35 feet in height above the level of the river at low water, and forms the section of a circle of 175 feet in diameter. The bridge, on account of the high ground on each side, is not visible from the turnpike road, and many travellers have, in consequence, passed it by unawares, and been disappointed of the pleasure of beholding it. In ascending the vale, it is approached by a road which turns abruptly to the left over the canal, a short distance above the Bridgewater Arms. The architect of this bridge, which formed, at the time of its erection, with very few exceptions, the largest arch in the world, was William Edwards, a self-taught genius, who never received the least assistance or instruction in his craft from a master.

CARDIFF CANAL, near Caerphilly, Energlyn, *John Goodrich*, Esq.

WHITCHURCH, 1 m. before, Green Meadow, Rev. *W. Lewis.*

From Cardiff		From Aberyst.
	Near Builth,	
	Cross the river Wye	
58½	*BUALT or BUILTH,*	43¾
	Brecknockshire	
	To Llandovery 22¼ m.	
	to Hay 19 m.	
51	Upper Chapel	51¼
47¼	Lower Chapel	55
45	Llandivilog	57¼
42¼	* BRECON	60
	to Abergavenny 20 m. and to Hay 15¼ m.	
	Cross the river Uske	
	To Llandovery 20 m. To Llangadock 23½ m. and to Neath 27 m.	
30½	Capel Nant Taff	71¾
	Coed y' Cummar,	
26	*Glamorganshire*	76¼
24	MERTHYR TYDVIL	78¼
16	Quaker's Yard, *Tavern*	86¼
	Near the Duke of Bridgewater's Arms,	
	To Llantrissent 4½ m.	
11	The Bridgewater Arms	91¼
	Cross the Cardiff canal	
3¼	Whitchurch	99
	* CARDIFF	102¼

the centre of which stands the town-hall, with the covered market underneath, an edifice that was built by subscription in the year 1762. The church, though plain, is a neat and very respectable modern structure, in the form of an oblong square, with a quadrangular stone tower and turrets. Rhayadergwy has a voice in the election of a parliamentary representative for New Radnor, and has also a good weekly market on Wednesday, besides three great markets in May.

BUILTH. *Thomas Price,* Esq.

MERTHYR TYDVIL, near, Cyfarthfa, ———.

CARDIFF is situated on the river Taff, over which there is a handsome bridge of five arches, and consists of two parishes, but has now only one church, the other having been destroyed by an inundation in the year 1607, together with many other buildings: its architecture offers little worthy of observation, except the arch of the west door, which is rich and handsome; its tower was erected in the reign of Edward III., and is a lofty square building of great beauty, surmounted at the corners by open pinnacles, greatly admired for their elegance and exquisite workmanship. This town, which is well built, has been the scene of many remarkable actions and events. Cardiff, together with Cowbridge, Swansea, Lougher, Aberavon, Kenfigg, Neath, and Llantrissent, sends one member to parliament. The markets on Wednesday and Saturday are well supplied with all kinds of provisions.

57 The Coach Time Table for the Aberystwyth to Cardiff route as it appeared in 'Patersons Roads'.

To quote from an old Welsh poem:-

'Ban wyr Bohun a oru
Gwaed fel mor bros Faenor fu'

'The Battle was won by the men of Bohun
And blood like an ocean in Vaynor was seen'.

It has always been considered that the dead from the battle were buried in the mound previously mentioned at Cae Burdydd (The field of the Slaughter). The mound had attracted the attention of past antiquarians who thought it may perhaps have been an ancient tumulus. With this in mind it was excavated in 1823 without any notable discoveries. In the opinion of the writer it is nothing more than a motte on which the first wooden castle would have been built, and which was the boundary bone of contention between the two Marcher Lords.

In 1290 Edward I called upon the two warring earls to appear before him at Abergavenny, when they were both taken into custody and their lands

THE NORTH VIEW OF MORLASHE CASTLE, IN THE COUNTY OF GLAMORGAN.

THIS Castle is situated on the Northern Edge of the County of Glamorgan, where it joyns with the County of Brecon, not far from the Road which leads from Brecon to Cardiffe. There are two small Rivers called Tave-Vaur and Tave-Vachan, which having taken their Rise in the Mountains of Brecnockshire, and running South into Glamorganshire, empty themselves into the River-Taf on which Llandaff and Cardiffe stands; and near the Confluence of these Rivers, on the North side of Tave-Vachan, this Castle is seated. Which is the Property of Mifs Lewis.

Sam'll. & Nath'l. Buck delin. et sculp. Publish'd according to Act of Parliamt. March 25th. 1741.

58 A view of Morlais Castle as it appeared in 1741. From a facsimile copy of an engraving in Buck's Antiquities.

58A Morlais Castle. The Crypt, the only remaining structure showing superb Norman fan vaulting. *Jack Evans.*

59 Sketch of the mound (motte) at Cae Burdydd, with Morlais Quarries and the remains of Morlais Castle on the eastern side of the valley. *Mansel Jones.*

101

confiscated. But in 1292 Edward relented and their lands and their liberty were restored on the payment of a heavy fine.

From Cae Burdydd one overlooks the Vaynor Church and churchyard. The only part now remaining of the Old Church is the castellated tower, the nave and chancel having fallen into decay. The first wooden church was built in 874AD, but this was burnt down during the boundary squabbles between the Norman lords. A new one, of stone, was built in 1295. Theophilus Jones writing in the latter part of the eighteenth century gives the following description:— "There is no village or even a single house adjoining the church; the roads in the approach to it are impassable by carriages and cannot without danger be travelled on horseback unless it be upon the small sure-footed ponies of the country. This building having a small tower with two bells and consisting of a nave and chancel only is low and dark, the roof not ceiled, the floor of earth and uneven, the seats decayed and irregular, and yet it is stated, twice a year upon oath to be in good and sufficient repair; perhaps this assertion may be here correct, for the situation is so inaccessible, and the dissenters in this parish are so numerous that the church, thus placed at the extremity of the district, and on the verge of another county, may be thought unnecessary or at least sufficient for the congregation!"

The dissenters referred to were the followers of Howell Harris, the Methodist leader who made periodic visits to Vaynor and the surrounding districts as did John Wesley and other revivalist leaders. These men had a profound effect on the religious life of the nation. An excellent account of the growth of Unitarianism and the history of one of the early Welsh

60   Vaynor Old Church.

61 The Vaynor Church and the remains of the Old Church, with the Church Tavern
close-by.   *Jack Evans.*

Unitarian Churches in our area is given in "Hen Dy Cwrdd, Cefn Coed y
Cymmer" written by Tom Lewis (Mab y Mynydd).

The present Vaynor Church was opened and consecrated in 1870, and the
cost of building was defrayed by Robert Thompson Crawshay, the former
ironmaster of Cyfarthfa Castle, Merthyr. He was buried in the churchyard
and his grave can be seen close to the church, a huge ten ton Radyr stone
slab, surrounded by iron railings. On the stone a brief yet eloquent
inscription reads in these poignant words "God forgive me".

The old burial ground of the church is now sadly neglected, many of the
headstones standing askew, some lying on the ground and almost all covered
with lichen and mosses. But for those interested in past history, a walk
around these thickly dotted graves perusing the inscriptions on the stones
will well repay the inconveniences of walking through clay and briars. On the
east wall of the tower of the old church is the tablet of Rhys Howel Rhys
which reads:—

Underneath
Lie the remains of Rhys Howel Rhys
of this Parish (Stone cutter)
Who died August 22nd 1817; aged 73 years.

Though born in humble life, without education, this man acquired
extensive knowledge in Astronomy, Poetry, Mathematics and Natural
Philosophy; unassuming in manners, and inactive in disposition, his talents

103

were known to a few admirers of native genius, who have placed this tribute to his memory:—

> Full many a flower is born to blush unseen,
> And waste its sweetness on the desert air.

> 'Nol ing a gwewyr angau,
> 'Ddryllio fy mhriddellau;
> Rhwng awyr, daear, dwr a than,
> Mi ymrana'n fan ronynau.   R.H.

Rhys Howel Rhys was born in Blaen-y-Glais Farm (O.S. 038109) situated on the western bank of the Glais Brook. It was here that Griffith Jones, Rector of Llanddowror, Carmarthenshire set up one of his Circulating Schools. Although Jones's intention was to educate and save the souls of his countrymen, his great achievement was to save the life of the Welsh language. He taught the nation to read and to write from the only text book that was readily available – the Welsh Bible. Schools were held in one thousand four hundred and seventy four (1,474) places in Wales, 105 of which were in Breconshire with 9 of these in the parish of Vaynor.

In 1738, the first full year of the Schools, they were as follows:—

Blaen y Glais in Vaynor	70 pupils
Vaynor ,,	39 pupils
Taff Fechan in Llandetty (Dolygaer)	54 pupils
Taff Vaynor ,,	41 pupils

62   Blaen-y-Glais Farm in Vaynor as it appeared in 1960. This circulating school of Rev. Griffith Jones had 70 pupils in 1738.   *John Yates.*

The total of 204 compared with 109 in Merthyr and 45 in Pant gives a clear indication of the relative importance of the two places prior to the industrial revolution which was to take place in Merthyr Tydfil from the latter half of the 18th century onwards.

It is a salutary and chastening experience to nowadays gaze upon the relatively small farm of Blaen-y-Glais in its splendid isolation alongside the upper reaches of the Glais and amongst the bare Vaynor mountains, and to compare the meagre education obtainable in those past times with the infinitely varied and greater opportunities of today.

But to return to the churchyard. A headstone commemorating another self-taught man with native talent, was erected by Rose Mary Crawshay, herself an intimate friend of many of the most learned people of the day.

The inscription reads:—

Thomas Norbury
was born at Bromsgrove
Died at Merthyr, July 14th 1872
Aged 64.

For 49 years he kept a small oil shop in Pont Storehouse, over which he built an observatory.

> "Skilful in all wisdom, and cunning in knowledge,
> and understanding science".

> "He spake of trees, from the cedar that is in Lebanon,
> and even unto the hyssop that springeth out of the wall;
> he spake also of the beasts, and of the fowl, and of
> creeping things".

> "After the way which they called heresy, so worshipped he
> the God of his fathers".

In Memoriam,
Rose Mary Crawshay.

On the west wall of the church is a memorial stone to a remarkable woman, Catherine Morgan. On it is inscribed:—

> "Catherine, the widow of David Morgan of Rhymney, who died
> on the 23rd day of February 1794, aged 106. She was born
> in the 3rd year of King James 2nd, and lived under seven
> reigns. Her husband died in 1746. She survived him for
> nearly fifty years".

On another of the tombstones in the churchyard is the rhyme:—

> 'Here lies the body of Gruffydd Shôn
> Covered here with earth and stone,
> You may sweep it up or leave it alone,
> It will be just the same to Gruffydd Shôn'.

The story goes that Gruffydd John died of a broken heart when his sweetheart married another suitor. At least someone brought a touch of humour to this enduring theme of fickle constancy.

These are just a few of the gravestones that encapsulate an interesting story or give an insight into the way of life of the people in bygone times.

Social life before the reservoirs

Perhaps a lasting impression one would now have of the two valleys are picturesque reservoirs resembling a miniature Lake District, with the surrounding hills covered by conifers. Prior to the development of these reservoirs, the valley floors were occupied by farmland, the Tithe Map of 1840 giving the following figures:—

Cwmtaf — 75% under grass, 14% arable, the remainder woodland, bracken and rough ground.

Vaynor — 43.5% pasture, 27% meadow, 20% arable and the remainder woodland and rough ground.

These figures did not include the common land which was widely used by all farmers for rough grazing. The maps on p. 109 give a clear indication of the changes from a completely agricultural way of life to one in which the growing iron and coal industries of Merthyr were having their social and topographical impact.

A few chosen verses of a free translation of a Welsh poem 'Can yr Hwsmon' written in 1750 by Howel Rhys, a Vaynor farmer and father of the previously mentioned Rhys Howel Rhys, will amply illustrate the life of the times.

THE FARMER'S SONG

Ye honest, gentle people,
Come, listen to my song;
I grow the corn to make the bread
That makes you hale and strong.

The landlord, will want a rent
Before he'll let the farm,
And should I trespass o'er the bounds
I'll surely come to harm.

Then I must have some money too
To hire me men to sow,
And horses, sheep and cows to buy,
And oxen for the plough.

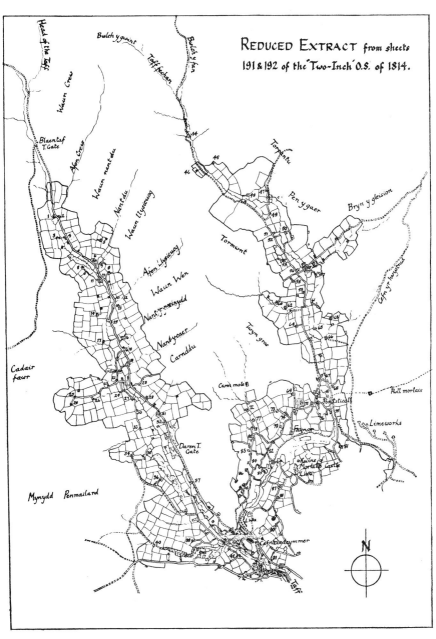

63 The map shows the extensive field pattern and the numerous farms in the two
valleys.

To fetch the coal and lime, I trow,
A handy lad I'll need,
Who'll turn the soil, manure it
Before I sow the seed.

And when the thresher comes around
Of busy work there's plenty;
To thresh, to fan, to clean the wheat,
And I pay him one in twenty.

Then to the mill the corn is borne,
And there the meal is ground;
For every fifteen I take home
The miller keeps a pound.

The parson takes his tithing
From pantry, fold, and field,
The smith, shoemaker, tailor,
The weaver, fuller, nailor
Reduce the farmer's yield.

When May-day comes, my workmen,
Will all expect their pay;
The landlord will demand his rent
Strict on St. Michael's Day.

Many old limekilns can still be found on the mountains where limestone was burnt, mostly using wood, which was plentiful, as a fuel. The lime which was thus readily available as a fertilizer for the local farmers, was also transported north to the old red sandstone areas. This brought an extra source of income to the hard-worked farmers. One can also understand from the poem that the economy was self-contained, primarily concerned with producing most of the requirements of the community. Local weavers supplied the flannel and cloth, which may have been augmented by some bought at the fairs, while ironwork of all kinds, from ploughs to nails was made by the smith, as were carts and waggons by the wheelwright. A carpenter made the furniture and clocks, and there were local shoe-makers, tailors and dressmakers. Other articles would be made at home on the hearth, on winter nights such as baskets and handles for various implements, while the women would be busy spinning, knitting and sewing.

It must be remembered that during these early times, although most of the shoemakers were good local craftsmen, leather footwear was almost unobtainable and would certainly be very expensive. Tom Lewis in his book 'Hen-dŷ-Cwrdd — Cefn Coed-y-Cymmer' recounts how Ann Jones a maidservant at Blaen Tâf Farm, Cwmtaf in the early part of the 19th Century, in order to "save" her shoes walked from Blaen Tâf to the first houses at the top of Cefn Coed in her bare feet. She would then put them on

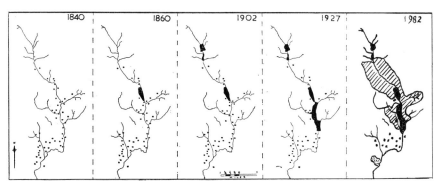

64 Tâf Fechan valley—Diagrams showing the progressive decrease in the number of
farms from 1840 to 1982.   *After Gillian Bale*

•.   Farmhouse the nucleus of farmed land

▨   Acreage leased by Forestry Commission

▥   Development of housing—Trefechan

◼   Tâf Fechan waterworks

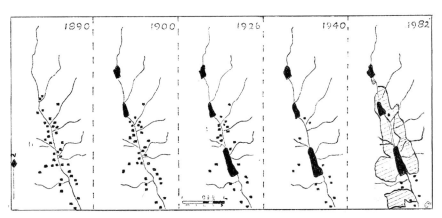

65 Tâf Fawr valley—Diagrams showing the progressive decrease in the number of
farms from 1890 to 1982.

•.   Farmhouse—each a nucleus of farmed land

◼   Cardiff Corporation reservoirs

▨   Acreage owned by Forestry Commission

to appear in the chapel with some semblance of respectability, while off they
would come again to tramp the six miles back home.

The footwear generally used were clogs which were made from alder trees
growing prolifically alongside the rivers and streams, as they still do. Alder is
the best wood for clog soles, being water resistant, soft and readily carved.
The itinerant cloggers would set up their camps and gradually work their way
through the woods. The trees were felled with an axe and the bole sawn into
four sizes- men's, women's, children's and young children's. They were then

109

'dressed' with an axe, the surplus bark removed, and the clog blocks seasoned in stacks. The final shaping of the block to suit each wearer's foot was carried out with a very sharp clogger's knife, specially honed for the purpose. This was a remarkable instrument which consisted of a strong, broad blade with a long projecting handle and was worked with a levering action. In skilled hands the shaping process followed precise dimensions.

Cloggers camps finished in the two valleys in the early 1900's, but they were still to be seen in other parts of rural Wales thirty or forty years ago, most of the clogs then being sent to Lancashire or Cheshire.

Alongside the Tâf Fechan near Cefn Coed-y-Cymmer (036085) one of the old fulling mills can still be seen, while at Pontsarn opposite the mouth of the Glais are the old ruins of a corn mill with a large grinding mill stone lying flat and broken nearby. Two other mills which ground corn were situated near the river's edge at Y Garn (Pontsticill).

The local farmers supplied the weaver with the raw wool, which then had to be graded, sorted, scoured and dried. The next process was carding, that is, combing, in order to align the wool fibres. This was first done with the hooked, spiny heads of teasles, but in later years with a wire brush. After carding, the fibres were spun into thread which was then dyed and woven into cloth.

At the fulling mills, which in Wales were known by the name *Pandy,* the cloth to be treated was put into tubs filled with alkali (caustic soda) or urine, and vigorously kneaded either by hand or mechanically. The mechanical kneaders were known as 'stocks' and were a sort of wooden trip-hammer operated by a water wheel.

66 Remains of the fulling mill on the Tâf Fechan river at Cefn-Coed-y-Cymmer.
Jack Evans

67 The Water Wheel on the Criban Brook, Pontsticill. This wheel worked the threshing machine of Abercriban Farm.

Finally, after stretching and drying, the nap of the cloth was raised by rubbing with boards covered with teasel heads. Thus was produced the well known *flannel* which is derived from the Welsh gwlanen from gwlân — wool. In the village of Cefn Coed-y-Cymmer some of the older inhabitants still boast that they have blankets and bed covers made in the local factories. Others still recall their parents telling them of a special cart collecting the urine from the houses. These were the days when 'pots' were an absolute essential in every household.

As in the past, limestone is still being quarried, but on a larger scale and for a different purpose. The one quarry still in production is the large Vaynor Quarry near Cefn Coed-y-Cymmer, which mainly produces stone for roads although some is ground to a dust for agricultural purposes. There are now no lime-burning kilns in the area, and the last of these can be seen deserted on the west facing scree-covered slope of Cilsanws Mountain in the Tâf Fawr Valley.

The Reservoirs

TÂF FECHAN

With the fast growth of Merthyr as an industrial town and the later increase of the population in Cardiff, a pure and regular supply of water was needed. And where better and easier to impound the water than in the valleys of the

Tâf Fawr and Tâf Fechan. During the mid-nineteenth century the only supply of water was from springs and wells, and this allied to the insanitary conditions that prevailed made cholera in South Wales towns a serious and frequent occurrence. Some extracts from the *Merthyr Express* of 1866, when a cholera epidemic from the 24th August to the 20th October accounted for the death of 115 people in Merthyr, will amplify the unhygienic conditions prevailing at the time. *November 3rd Editorial:* "We believe that disease broke out because of filth, overcrowding, bad ventilation, poor and bad food and the vicious habit of drunkeness". *September 20th – Local Intelligence* "A Cefn Coed man complained to the Inspector that a neighbour with stinking pig-wash close to the house had left it untouched for six weeks. The neighbour eventually removed it and took it into the house, where it probably now remains".

The Merthyr Tydfil Local Board of Health established the first reservoir in 1858, the Pentwyn Reservoir or Dolygaer Lake as it came to be known, in the Tâf Fechan valley. Very soon with the rapid expansion of industries, more water was needed, and the two reservoirs further north were built in 1884 and 1902 – the Lower Neuadd and the Upper Neuadd respectively. The latter was called the Zulu because of its construction during the Zulu war. To complete the saga of reservoir building in this valley it was discovered that the dam of Dolygaer Lake was constructed on the Neath geological fault, resulting in a serious seepage of water from the reservoir. In 1913 plans were made by the Tâf Fechan Water Board to construct a fourth reservoir immediately south of Pentwyn, this to merge the two into the Pontsticill reservoir and to give a body of water 2½ miles long. Because of the delay caused by World War I it was not completed until 1927. The construction of the reservoir involved the submergence of land belonging to eight farms, some cottages and small holdings, the vicarage, Capel Tâf Fechan – the 15th century Dolygaer Church – and a Congregational chapel.

The *Merthyr Express,* July 23rd 1927 records the event "On the bed of the great lake was a picturesque hamlet slumbering between the verdant hills of Pontsticill. Buried beneath the glistening waters are several cottages, once the homes of humble but happy families. And there lives in those gloomy depths a quaint village church and a Congregational Chapel, together with their respective graveyards. A valley of buried memories".

The Pontsticill reservoir can now be considered as one of the most picturesque sheets of water in Wales. The wood-clad mountains quietly enfold this seemingly large lake, while to the north the vista is ennobled by the majestic outline of the Brecon Beacons. It is a quiet, peaceful place, much used by walkers who escape into the surrounding hills from the industrial pressures of the valleys further south. But it is very difficult to imagine or equate the relatively small number of people which now visit the area with the vast gatherings who frequented the valley in the past.

When the Pentwyn reservoir was built it gave an added quality to the rich and farm-studded valley, contrasting wonderfully with the wild individuality of the Brecon Beacons mountain scenery further north. All this was brought within reach of the people when the Brecon and Merthyr Railway from Pant to Brecon was constructed in the years 1860-1863. Later it was to be extended from Pontsticill to Cefn Coed in 1867 and finally into Merthyr in 1868.

These were the days when catchment areas for reservoirs were not considered the sacrosanct stretches of land that they were later to become. It is only within the last ten years that the various Water Authorities have relaxed their exceedingly stringent controls and allowed what is now termed "multi-purpose usage" on some of the reservoirs. The Merthyr Tydfil Sailing Club, for example, now use parts of the Pontsticill Reservoir for boating activities, while the old Pentwyn Reservoir section, a Nature Reserve with the Brecknock Naturalists' Trust, provides facilities for the Naturalists and fishermen only, with the latter having the use of all the reservoirs.

The Pentwyn Reservoir became a mecca for those wanting to escape into the countryside from the fast developing urban areas. The newspapers of the time tell the story very vividly, and as early as 1862 there were many excursions advertised to alight at Torpantau and enjoy plentiful refreshments at Pentwyn Inn together with boating and fishing on the Lake. The Merthyr Express (28/7/1865) writes anticipating a rural fête at Pentwyn "The charming locality of our reservoir we are glad to notice is to be the scene of a rural fete a week or two hence all being well and the weather fine. A better spot could not have been selected and as the programme will embrace aquatic as well as terrafirma sports and pastimes we have no doubt that the fête will be largely patronised, especially by the young of Merthyr and Dowlais".

Unfortunately, as so often happens, our variable weather played a major role and their report (11/8/1865) reads, "The Pentwyn Fete came off yesterday, but a drizzling rain which set in just about the time that the visitors began to pour into Dolygaer, interfered with the proceedings sadly. The ardour of the pleasure-seekers however, was not seriously damped, and such of the games as could be taken up were entered into with zest. The boat race came off with great *eclat*, and there was a whole fleet of boats on the water. Large numbers indulged themselves in dancing at the Pentwyn Inn. The attendance was most respectable and there were about 400 people on the grounds". In the same year great things were envisaged for the pleasure-seeking public and a momentous event was about to take place as reported in the Merthyr Express (2/9/1865) "The steamer that 'is to be' on the Pentwyn Reservoir is rapidly advancing towards completion. The cabin has already been constructed, and a part of the machinery for propelling the boat through the water is in the building alongside, in which the hull of the boat is moored. The remainder is expected to arrive shortly, and then no time will be lost in rigging out the little steamer for her wedding to the lake, which will certainly be lordly enough for her".

The Merthyr Telegraph of 26th August 1865 wrote "Ere long a veritable *Steamer* is to plough the waves of Pentwyn and glide like a thing of life on

68 The search for pleasure and recreation late in the 19th century did not entail travelling far afield. Chapel and Church committees were quite satisfied to spend their annual Sunday School outing either at Pontsarn, Dolygaer or Storey Arms, Cwmtaf. The photograph shows the adults and children of Ebenezer Chapel, Cefn-Coed-y-Cymmer, taken outside Pentwyn House, Dolygaer, on the occasion of their outing there in 1895.

69   Tabor Chapel Sunday School Party at Dolygaer in 1904.

that eternal mirror of everlasting hills. A steamer under the shadow of the Beacons! We fling down the pen, lost in wonder and expectancy."

The boat successfully plied passengers around the lake but suffered serious mishap as reported in the Merthyr Express (29/6/1867). "The steam packet which was built two or three years ago to ply on the lake of Pentwyn for the accommodation of visitors and excursionists, owing to carelessness and the severe storm of last winter, sank in about 30 feet of water, so that no trace of her was seen. No attempt was made to raise her until last week, when Mr. T. Jepson, contractor of Dowlais, undertook the difficult task of raising her from the water. Without the aid of divers he commenced his dangerous task, put on several hands with sufficient pulleys and other necessary tackle for the purpose, and after working hard for about twenty hours succeeded in getting the packet in sight to the joy of the proprietor Mr. F. Atkins and all present. In less than two hours afterwards the packet was afloat and ready to take a voyage around the reservoir which was accomplished with several persons on board".

The Mr. F. Atkins mentioned was Mr. Frederick Atkins "of Pengelly Fawr and Pentwyn, Farmer and Auctioneer" (Merthyr Telegraph 22/1/1870) who had the fishing and boating rights at the reservoir and as "Captain" Atkins commanded the steam-boat.

A regatta held on the 4th July 1867 and described by the Merthyr Express, (13/7/1867), shows what an active part the steamer played in the outings at the reservoir. "Next to the Flower Show in popularity in Merthyr is the Pentwyn Regatta. The former is the grand fete for our fashionables, the latter the holiday par excellence of the people; both are of recent origin, and both at present give signs of permanence . . . . . . The construction of the

115

reservoir of Pentwyn led to the development amongst us of what we may truly call the national taste – a love of boating. No sooner was the reservoir well in working order than boats were launched upon it. Three regattas have taken place there, and scarcely a day now passes that does not see its pleasure parties at Pentwyn, and the boats on the water filled with the young and old of both sexes, from all classes of society . . . . . . The regattas at Pentwyn have always excited great interest in the neighbourhood, and attracted thousands of spectators . . . . . . The day was observed as a general holiday in Merthyr and Dowlais, most of the tradesmen having closed their shops before one o'clock, while many did not open at all. The roads to the Pant Station were thronged all day, and the Railway Company had as much as it could do to work the traffic between Pant and Pentwyn with anything like punctuality and safety . . . . . . between 3,000 and 4,000 people were conveyed to Pentwyn and back that day without a single accident.

"Not all who went to Pentwyn travelled by rail. The roads swarmed with people in vehicles and on foot, and at places, afforded a feeble illustration of the road from London to Epsom on Derby Day. We should say that there were about 6,000 persons on the ground during the afternoon. These were nearly all congregated on a field above the reservoir and on the east side, where the refreshment booths were erected and every huckster who had traffic to ply put up his standing . . . . . . The two Cyfarthfa bands – the brass and drum and fife were on the ground during the whole of the afternoon and performed long programmes of music with their accustomed ability. The sound of the music as it floated from one bank to the other was exquisite.

"One of the greatest objects of interest to thousands of spectators was the steamer, which had been raised from the bottom a fortnight previously. Nearly forty 'voyages' were made by this wonderful craft during the day''. No account could better recapture for us the excitement, gaiety and the promise of a rapturous day in the country at the Pentwyn Regatta than that which appeared in the Merthyr Express of July 7th 1866: – "If we wanted a proof for the strong desire for out-of-door amusement on the part of a people stuck up between high hills in the middle of a smoky, dusty, dirty town, we had it a week on Thursday. On that day Merthyr seemed forsaken, business came to a deadlock for the time being, everyone hoped to be at the regatta. What! a regatta between these Welsh hills? says some friends sneeringly who have been brought up in a seaport town. Yes certainly – one that attracted more people than perhaps any other event of the year. One reason for this was self-evident. Pentwyn grounds were free for all, and the Brecon and Merthyr Railway, who very obligingly took passengers to and fro for an insignificant "joey" (a threepenny bit).

Did we need any other reasons more cogent than these we should find it in the fact that our toiling and sweating brethren eagerly longed for the opportunity of inhaling the fresh air and enjoying the lovely mountainous scenery in the vicinity of Pentwyn.

70 Dolygaer Farm and the family of the late Mr and Mrs Job Morgan. Teas were
also served at the farm.

"Hence it was that by rail and road, thousands started off for this regatta. Everything capable of carrying human beings, inside or out, was pressed into service . . . . . . Superfine broad cloth and coarse fustian, glace silks and faded gingham, struggled for a place in the railway carriages, or if less fortunate, were huddled into a mineral brake van like so many cattle, for which the company was not responsible . . . . . . nearly 11,000 people had congregated on the grassy slope at the side of the lake at the time when the sports had begun. To minister to their pleasure and to their appetites, marquees, booths and stalls had been erected which did a thriving trade . . . . . . We should observe that the Cyfarthfa Brass Band under George Livesey took up its station on the right bank at the foot of the slope, and the fife and drum band was beside the brass. The Brass Band played some excellent pieces from Verdi, Rossini, Meyerbeer and other masters . . . . . .

The Bristol and Cardiff crews were entertained most sumptuously in Mr. Crawshay's private tent . . . . . . a repast of a solid nature was flanked up by the choicest fruits, including new figs, bananas, peaches etc., from the Cyfarthfa conservatories''.

71 Pontsarn Station was a scene of much life and bustle in the summer months when Pontsarn was the rendezvous of Sunday School treats

Tâf Fawr

The bottom-land in the Cwmtaf portion of the Tâf Fawr was rich, and the farms were many – twenty-two holdings, making it a well-stocked landscape of cattle and sheep. Most of the farms were small, and interspersed among these were the small-holdings, sufficient for one or two cows, a few sheep, a few pigs and poultry. The tithe survey of 1840 describing the holdings, illustrates the essential features of this self-supporting community:-

9 were less than 10 acres
12 were between 10 and 200 acres
1 was over 200 acres.

In 1884 the Cardiff Corporation, because of insufficient supplies from reservoirs near the town, obtained permision to obtain water in the Tâf Fawr Valley. The first to be built was Cantref (the middle reservoir) in 1892, resulting in the loss of four large sheep farms, Glan Crew, Crew Isaf, Aber Crew and Blaen Tâf.

The Beacons reservoir, south of the Storey Arms, and situated in open mountain land, was the next completed in 1897.

But as with Merthyr and the valleys to the south, the rapid growth of industry and the increase in the population of Cardiff made it imperative that more water be impounded. Thus, the largest reservoir Llwyn-On, originally scheduled for 1915 but, as with Pontsticill reservoir, delayed by the outbreak of World War 1, was not completed until 1926.

This reservoir literally drowned the community. Here was the heart-land, the 'nucleated' village of Ynys-y-Felin, with a cluster of about twelve houses, a fulling mill and two local inns "The Red Lion" and the "Travellers". The hamlet, ever mindful of the religious life, included a baptist chapel, Capel Bethel, a plain squat building on the right bank of the river overlooking the valley. Immediately behind the chapel was a tiny burial ground, from where the bodies were exhumed prior to 1926 and re-interred in the grounds of the new Chapel which was built by the Cardiff Corporation on the eastern side of the valley, opposite the dam.

The old Parish road crossed the Tâf at Pont-ar-Dâf and continued towards Penderyn in front of the Chapel. Another picturesque old bridge can be seen on the western side of the reservoir inside the boundary railings. When the water in the reservoir is very low, Pont-ar-Dâf is resurrected and comes into view, with the river still following its old course under the bridge.

The limestone for the building of the three dams of the reservoirs was quarried at the Ffrwdd, on the western side of the valley. To transport the stone to the respective sites a mineral railway was built, locally called the 'Navvies Line'. This now makes a pleasant walk through the leafy glades of the Penmoelallt woodland.

72 The hamlet of Ynys-y-Felin as it appeared before the construction of Llwyn-On reservoir. The 'Farmer's Arms' is in the foreground.

Between Llwyn-On reservoir and Cantref at the confluence of Nant-ddu and Tâf Fawr was the smaller hamlet of Nant-Ddu. It consisted of the Church of St. Mary; the vicarage, one or two small holdings and two public houses, the Millers Arms and Tredegar Arms. The vicarage and the public houses were pulled down and the sites used for Cardiff Corporation houses. The presence of so many public houses and hostelries which are now sadly missing, denotes the past importance of the major Turnpike road from Merthyr to Brecon which has now developed into the main A470 trunk road.

The children were educated at a small Church of England school situated near the confluence of Nant Llysieuog and Tâf Fawr. This was closed in 1928 and the children transported to the Cefn Coed schools. Mention of Nant Llysieuog introduces another custom which has now succumbed to modern medical treatment. Still marked on ordnance maps near the source of the Llysieuog are the words Ffynnon Llysieuog (ffynnon = well). This denotes the presence of a mineral spring where many people, some from far afield, collected the water in jugs and urns and any suitable container in the firm

73 Photographs taken in the summer of 1959, showing Llwyn-On reservoir at very low water. Pont-ar-Dâf, normally under the water is still intact, with the river following its old course.

conviction that it cured most ailments, including constipation. Particularly was it good for removing impurities from the blood, and liberal doses were taken during the Spring season. Anyone who has walked to the site in an endeavour to discover the old well will quickly realise that to even get there the people must have been extraordinarily fit.

Transport

The coming of the railways to the South Wales valleys, had a tremendous impact on the social life of the people, and the industrial development of the whole region. Merthyr and Dowlais, with the rapid increase of population,

74   The railway station at Pontsticill in 1900, and a view of the valley before the impounding of the water for the Tâf Fechan reservoir. The Brecon Beacons are in the background.

needed the agricultural produce of the rich farmland to the north, whilst the rural areas were in need of the coal, lime and industrial products of the towns in the South. Moreover, day trips to the countryside became possible, including even the more distant pleasure trips to the mineral springs of Mid Wales.

The contractors responsible for the making of the Brecon and Merthyr Railway, Messrs. Davies, Savin and Ward made a start at Torpantau at the beginning of 1860. Here a tunnel was to be built through a ridge separating the Caerfanell Valley (Glyn valley) from the Tâf Fechan valley, and they commenced excavating from either side.

The work was done by navvies using picks, shovels, barrows, horses and carts, labouring in conditions that would now be considered primitive, to say the least. Finally, in January 1862, the two gangs working from opposite ends made a breach to allow a free passage from one side to the other. It speaks volumes for the accuracy of the engineers of the time, that on measuring the line of the bore which was 666 yards long, the two centres co-incided within two inches.

In the meantime the work had been proceeding on the sections of the line to Pant and Brecon respectively, and 1863 heralded the opening for passengers and goods traffic along the whole 19 miles between Brecon and Pant.

The primary aim was to get the line to Merthyr, but in 1863 the only connection with Merthyr was by means of a horse-bus from Pant. It was not until 1867 that the railway proceeded as far as Cefn Coed and in the same year the section from Pant to Dowlais Top was publicly opened.

The Merthyr Express (3/8/1867) includes the following report:- "The opening of the Cyfarthfa branch of the Brecon and Merthyr Railway to Cefn station took place on Thursday the 1st instant. There was no display about the opening — nothing at all like the opening of the line to Pant — and the trains ran to and from with as little ceremony as if they had been running that way a dozen years. There was of course, a little excitement in Cefn, and a great number of people assembled to witness the arrival and departure of the first train. We hope the line will be speedily opened right through to Merthyr. The Company can hardly be blind to the enormous loss which they sustain by the present unserviceable state of the line". With the opening of the Cefn section, Pontsticill Junction came into being, and Cefn Coed replaced Pant as a terminus for the horse-bus. A very fine stone viaduct was built at Pontsarn to span the river Tâf Fechan, 455ft. long, 92ft. high with seven arches and a large abutment at the Merthyr end.

The long delay getting to Merthyr was caused by the intransigence of William Crawshay who adamantly refused to allow the engineers to plot a route on the eastern side of the valley through the Cyfarthfa Castle grounds. Alexander Sutherland, an engineer and bridge-builder together with Henry Conybeare, consulting engineer, both employed by the B. & M., surveyed a much more expensive route from Cefn to Merthyr along the western side of the river Tâf Fawr. Another stone viaduct, built on a curve, was required to

75 The narrow gauge train of the Brecon Mountain Railway at Pontsticill station.
The Tâf Fechan reservoir is in the background.   *Jack Evans*

carry the line over the Tâf Fawr, which was 770 ft. long, 121ft. at the highest point, and consisted of 15 arches with a 39′ 6″ span.

The Merthyr Express (1/9/1866) commemorates the opening event thus:- "On Monday last the interesting ceremony of fixing the last brick in the last arch of this stupendous and magnificent specimen of engineering skill was performed most gracefully by Mrs. Sutherland, the wife of the local Engineer who was presented by the masons with a handsome silver trowel for that purpose. At the conclusion of the ceremony Mr. Sutherland entertained a select party at luncheon". This viaduct, apart from being a superb engineering feat, is one of the most aesthetic examples of stone-masonry building in the land. It is now a national monument, most worthy of preservation for future generations to admire 19th century craftsmanship. In August 1868 the Merthyr to Brecon line was completed for public service as the Merthyr Express (8/8/1868) recounts:- "On Saturday last, without scarcely a notice to apprise the public of the event, the long looked-for opening of the Brecon and Merthyr Railway into the Vale of Neath station took place; and on that morning a passenger train ran for the first time all the way from Brecon to Merthyr". How many at this time could possibly foresee that in less than a hundred years it would be closed and the age of steam would come to an end. But in this relatively short period the B. & M. built for itself a tradition, character and charm that far outshone many of its bigger and illustrious companies. Poems and plays have been written about it, humorous stories and whimsical anecdotes remembered and retold. Typical

76   The Cefn-Coed-y-Cymmer viaduct during construction, showing the substantial and solid wooden scaffolding.

77   The Heads of the Valleys road bridge which spans the Tâf Fechan at Cefn Coed y Cymmer, under construction.   *John Yates*

125

78 Aerial photograph taken in 1958 of the Cefn-Coed-y-Cymmer viaduct. The railway station and sidings are on the extreme left and the site of the Pont-y-Capel Brewery is on the immediate right of Pont-y-Capel Bridge.   *John Yates*

of these is an account of an episode published in the *Field* of 31/10/1868:-(vol xxxii, No 827). A fisherman caught in Llangorse Lake a large pike weighing 22lbs. It showed remarkable endurance, for it was kept alive in the water of the lake for two days and then sold to one of the engine drivers on the Brecon and Merthyr. This gentleman proposed to take the fish to Newport. Eventually the pike was brought "from the lake (Llangorse) a mile distant, in a wetted bag to the station (Talyllyn)". The engine driver was now in a quandary and had to decide what was to be done with the fish. One of the Brecon and Merthyr inspectors rose to the occasion, crying "put him in the tender, Jack!". At once the fish was "emptied out" into the man-hole of the locomotive tender and soon recovered its strength in the fresh water. The pike survived the rough transit to Newport and there its final fate is lost to posterity with the words of the man who went into the tender to get it out − "we had a deuce of a job to do it!".

A pen Sketch written by Tom Lewis (Mab-y-Mynydd) a local historian of Cefn-Coed-y-Cymmer, gives us a glimpse of one of the many 'characters' − the stationmaster at Cefn-Coed − who were such an intrinsic part of that unique railway − the Brecon and Merthyr. "Of the many characters who have long since left the earthly scene, few perhaps stand out in remembrance in bolder relief, than Mr. Lucas. So thorough was Mr. Lucas's allegiance to his employers that one could not escape the feeling that if "the Company" came to financial grief the catastrophe would change the course of history. This, however, can be truly said of him – no one served the "Company" better than did he. He was as much a part of the station as the signal box or the goods shed, and it would not be an overstatement to say that he regarded "the Company's premises" with that reverence with which one regards a graveyard.

Between him and the villagers he had set up an impenetrable barrier, for few were on intimate terms with him . . . . . As patience was not one of Mr. Lucas's strong points, nor toadying to the rich, one of his failings, a late passenger panting up the steep approach with only a second to spare to catch the train was given a stern lecture on the virtues of punctuality.

But it was on Bank Holidays that Mr. Lucas was to be seen disporting himself in all his official glory. On these auspicious days "my station" normally so sleepy, was transformed into a miniature Paddington. The most popular way at that time of spending a Bank Holiday was to go apicnicing to Pontsarn or Dolygaer. The station was crammed with shiny faced little boys in sailor suits and beribboned little girls in cheap, coloured pinafores. Perspiring mothers with their babies wound Welsh fashion around their shoulders, shouted excited orders to their older children to keep away from the platform edge.

In the hubbub, Mr. Lucas, his gold-braided cap sitting on his head with just a suspicion of a sporting angle, was a picture of futile industry. When the distant signal on the bend near Tai Mawr Road dropped, he clanged his hand-bell to indicate that the train had been sighted. The clanging in truth was wholly unnecesssry for the train was plainly seen and heard a mile away by all who had eyes to see and ears to hear. The fussy little engine, red as a pillar box, and its brass dome shining like burnished gold, clanked over the points at the end of the viaduct as if it were about to fall to pieces. The driver, known as "Hell Fire Jack" (because he drove at a speed of twenty miles an hour), leaned out of his cab with an air of responsibility that made every schoolboy on the platform green with envy. The "Pride of the Line" (that is what Mr. Lucas fondly called the engine) having been brought to a standstill with brakes screaming and escaping steam hissing, the excited crowd surged forward as if carried on shifting sands, and high above the din could be heard Mr. Lucas's commanding voice shouting, in not too elegant language, peremptory orders to "make room for women and children first."

The end of an era came with the last train on the Merthyr to Abergavenny line (which became the London and North Western Railway and finally the London, Midland and Scottish Railway) running on Sunday, 5th January 1958, and the last from Merthyr to Brecon (which became the Great Western Railway) in 1964.

But the nostalgic sound of the puffing engine and the shrill whistle refused to be silenced and white banners of steam are still to be seen in the Tâf Fechan Valley. The very practical railway enthusiasts of Hills and Rampton have stepped in, and since June 1980 one of the Little Trains of the newly

79   Train from Tal-y-Bont-on-Usk arriving at Torpantau Station before proceeding to Pontsticill station.   *Glyn Davies*

formed Brecon Mountain Railway Company has been plying on a narrow gauge line along the old route between Pant and Pontsticill. The Company intends to restore part of the delightful run alongside the Pontsticill reservoir to Torpantau, through the tunnel and into the steep-sided and majestic Glyn Collwn Valley.

Although the coming of the trains had made travel in the valleys much easier, they were used by most of the people only on particular occasions and as a special luxury. They could not afford the high fares and as very few possessed a horse, and fewer still, a carriage; men, women and children considered it no hardship to walk many miles daily, and this was a part of the work-a-day lives of miners, steelworkers and craftsmen of all kinds. Occasionally they rode in a horse bus or a brake, as recounted in the Merthyr Star of 1863 and Merthyr Telegraph of 1875: "Public coaches with a fare of one shilling would set out at Easter and Whitsun from the Lord Raglan Inn at Cefn and make the journey to Pentwyn Reservoir via Pontsarn. The route was so difficult and fraught with danger that, as one passenger wrote, it required 'an incessant use of the whip and a man walking alongside with a stick to spur on four wretched horses on the rough surface of the road'."

But some, obviously, would prefer the company and jollity of a horse-bus, with its many stops and starts to the more solemn and sedate ride on the trains, particularly if it happened to be a fraternal gathering of rugby

80   An outing on a horse-bus arriving at the Storey Arms at the head of Glyn Tarell.

players. All players of the oval ball can well imagine the hilarious times enjoyed by the occupants of this particular bus, passing three pubs on the way to their destination, and described in fairly prosaic terms in the Merthyr Express 18/4/1903. "Merthyr Thursdays had an enjoyable day at Brecon on Good Friday, and everyone voted it the most pleasant outing for a long time.

81   A coach about to set out on its journey.

Leaving Merthyr at 10.30 a.m. in Mr. Dix's well known turnout "The Imperial", the party reached Brecon in three hours. The country drive produced good appetites for the sumptuous spread prepared by hostess James at the Black Lion Hotel. A stroll around the town was indulged in before the game. After the game an excellent tea was partaken of, and then a rush to the boats – 'a wow on the wiver' as someone termed it. A few fatalities were only narrowly averted, especially when the genial secretary tried to shoot the rapids, and the captain attempted to run down the vice-captain who, by skillful handling of his canoe, saved a disastrous wreck". For the record, Merthyr even won the game!

These horse-drawn vehicles when in use were left open during the Summer, but a hood was used as a covering during the rest of the year. A tail-boy rode on the back steps to open the door and to take the fares.

Heavy goods were transported locally by horse and cart, and gambos were used for hay, corn, pigs, sheep and calves. Much material was carried on the backs and shoulders of men and the heads of women. It was a common sight

STOLEN,

FROM A STABLE ON COED-Y-CYMER

Late on Friday Night or very early on Saturday Morning last,

A BAY HORSE

OF THE SADDLE KIND,

Two years old last grass, about 13 hands high, Bald Face, two white spots on his poll close to the ears with a notch or mark in the left ear, Black mane and tail long not dock'd, two white feet behind with a white mark on the inside of the left foot before. The Horse was seen passing through Trecastle between 6 & 7 o'clock on Saturday morning last the 23rd Instant, the supposed thief was riding him bare back'd with an old halter in his head.

Whosoever will discover the offender so that he may be brought to Justice shall Receive

Five Guineas

REWARD,

By applying to THOMAS WILLIAM WALTER.

COED-Y-CYMMER 25th Nov. 1816.

W. WILLIAMS, PRINTER, MERTHYR TYDFIL

82   Such a considerable award emphasises the importance of horses when these were the only means of speedy transport.

83 The old Cefn-Coed-y-Cymmer bridge with an electric tram on the right of the picture, circa 1900. The trams could not travel into Cefn Coed until the new bridge was built.

in Cefn, even as late as the 1920's to see women carrying large baskets of washing or smaller baskets of garden produce or pig-swill on their heads. A towel was twisted into the form of a rope and coiled into a pad called a 'trochan' and placed on the head. This method is still employed by women in many parts of the world. Babies were invariably carried, snug and warm, suspended in shawls which were slung over a shoulder and tucked under the arm. Prams slowly made their appearance just prior to the 1st World War, and to begin with were certainly not the well-sprung, sophisticated carriages of today. Many will recall that during the miners strikes of 1921 and 1926 the

84 The Stocks, High Street, Cefn-Coed-y-Cymmer in 1914 showing the first Merthyr tram-car to arrive in the village.

coal was carried from the 'patches' (where coal-seams outcropped and could fairly easily be obtained) in sacks on the backs of the miners.

It was the coming of the electric tramway that provided a cheap form of public transport. The first tramway from Merthyr to Cefn was opened in 1900, but could only come as far as the old Cefn Bridge which crossed the river Tâf Fechan. The new Bridge was not built until 1910 and it took another four years for the first Merthyr tram-cars to arrive at the Cefn Coed terminus, situated at the northern end of the village.

The pace of technological development was now quickening and the internal combustion engine was taking over. Asphalt products also came to be used for surfacing roads, particularly 'tarmac' (derived from the name of Macadam), using crushed stone and tar poured hot on to a prepared road surface. Charabancs in the 1920's were quickly followed by the buses and in 1939 the tramcars were made redundant and the rails removed from the roads. After World War 11 and the dramatic expansion of the roads network to cope with the ever increasing road traffic, the Heads of the Valley road was built to link Merthyr with Abergavenny and eventually with Swansea and the West. It bisects the village of Cefn Coed, necessitating the spanning of the rivers Tâf Fawr and Tâf Fechan with modern concrete bridges. The Tâf Fechan bridge was the first in the country to be built using the balanced cantilever system of construction and both bridges were given a Civic Trust Award in 1968 for their graceful designs.

85   A party at the start of a charabanc outing.

The Village of Cefn-Coed-y-Cymmer

Cefn-Coed-y-Cymmer, the largest village in the area came into being in the early days of the industrial revolution that was taking place in Merthyr. Prior to this it was composed of a few dotted farmsteads and cottages. The ground on which it now stands was then a dense woodland on the confluence of the two rivers Tâf Fawr and Tâf Fechan. Trees were cut down, land was enclosed, and houses built from the local stone. The early smelting of iron required vast quantities of charcoal, so the woodlands began to disappear, except where the iron-masters required shelter and breeding areas for game (e.g. Penmoelallt woodland). Because of the very nature of its growth the area was unplanned, with the turnpike road forming the main thoroughfare.

The inns and taverns were numerous, with commodious yards and stables, showing that in its early days the village had been an important marketing centre on the route of the drovers; one of the inns remaining bears the name 'Drovers Arms'. Most of the inns, totalling twenty, were located in the main street, so providing a wide choice within a very short distance. It is rather intriguing that although nearly all the inhabitants of the village were Welsh speaking the names of the inns were practically all English:- Green Dragon, Greyhound, Drovers Arms, Rising Sun, Brecon and Merthyr Railway Inn, Cefn Hotel, Station Hotel, Castle Inn, Morning Sun, Cross Keys, Royal Oak, Rose and Castle, Bridgend, Pontycapel, Pontycapel Brewery, Railway Inn, Globe, White Horse, Greyhound Head, Farmers Arms, Crawshay Arms, Corner House, The George, Gwynne's Arms, Lord Raglan, Davies' Brewery. Two local breweries supplied most of the ale, one at Pont-y-Capel adjoining the Tâf Fawr and the other on the site of the present Ysgol-y-Graig School, by the side of the Tâf Fechan. Not only did they supply beer, but the spent barley grains in the fermenting process were eagerly collected for feeding the pigs, which were either kept in sites at the bottom of the garden, or in communal pig-sties built at the Wern, near the viaduct. These were the days when most people kept pigs, and their cured carcases were hung from hooks in the rafters of the ceiling. A prized possession with the boys of the village was the bladder of the pig, which was the only football they ever acquired.

The vast majority of the people baked their own bread, mostly in the three bake-houses in the village, and 'barm' which was the yeast froth from the fermenting liquor in the beer-making process, was collected from the breweries to leaven the home-made bread.

After World War 1, and the great and severe economic depression that overtook Merthyr and the valleys, due to the closure of the Cyfarthfa Iron Works, Dowlais Steelworks and the recession in the coal-pits, the two breweries struggled on unprofitably for a while, but eventually closed down, along with many of the pubs and the shops.

Many of the houses built during the early mushroom growth of the village when work was plentiful were now considered sub-standard and badly in

86   The High Street, Cefn-Coed-y-Cymmer circa 1895.

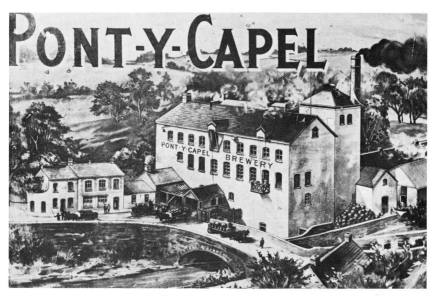

87   The Brewery and offices situated at the western end of Pont-y-Capel.

88   The first two-arched Pont-y-Capel. On the left of the bridge where the Brewery
later stood, is an old Mill. The old road (Job's Lane) can be seen on the right. From a
water colour painted by Penry Williams in 1825.

135

need of repair. They were replaced mostly by Council houses, and a small council estate was built in the village. After the second World War it was considered necessary to build another Council Estate, aptly named Tre-Fechan, outside the village and mid-way to Pontsarn. It too, is set amidst very pleasant natural surroundings, but unfortunately, is close to the expanding Vaynor Quarries.

A large firm, Teddington Aircraft Controls came to Cefn-Coed-y-Cymmer in the early post-war period (1945) but after a spell of local economic growth and full employment for the villagers, it was a very early victim of foreign competition and the developing recession in Europe.

We have followed briefly the story of our two Welsh upland valleys and the impact of man upon them from the first settlers of prehistoric times to the great technological advances of the present. We have witnessed the many changes that have taken place since the early travellers gave us accounts of the beauties and delights of the valley bottoms, contrasting so vividly with the fine landscapes and wild individuality of the uplands; of how rough roads and tracks gave way to better and faster routes. We have noted the dramatic changes that came about with the birth of the industrial revolution in Merthyr Tydfil; the sudden change from an agricultural economy with its slow traditional form of living, to one of hustle and bustle in fast-growing communities. The rich valley farmlands were flooded by much needed reservoirs, and the woodlands slowly disappeared. Railways came and went and a new arterial road for the fast moving traffic severed the village of Cefn Coed.

Fortunately huge expanses of peaceful and uncluttered landscape still remain inviolate, whilst the reservoirs have added their own quiet splendour to the rural scene. Hill walkers can still move in any direction where their compasses point to explore the more remote parts of our countryside. Unfortunately, there has been a steady erosion of the open uplands and the valley sides. Alien and monotonous blocks of conifers have intruded upon the best landscapes. For the naturalist, wild life in a wood of these evergreens is so much poorer than under trees that let in the light and shed their leaves. But although time and modern development have frayed some of the old fabric of these two fine valleys, we are fortunately still left with a relatively unspoiled and undeveloped countryside, so vitally necessary in this age of quick growth and harsh materialism. Even the poet William Cowper would be partly satisfied by what the valleys of Tâf Fechan and Tâf Fawr can offer:-

> "Oh for a lodge in some vast wilderness,
> Some boundless contiguity of shade,
> Where rumour of oppression and deceit,
> Of unsuccessful or successful war,
> Might never reach me more"

References

Theophilus Jones. The History of Brecknock. (Vol I).

Gillian M Bale. Cultural Changes in Cwmtaf 1840-1957. Cultural Changes in Tâf Fechan Valley 1840-1958. (Cefn Coed and Vaynor Local History Society).

Tom Lewis (Mab-y-Mynydd). Characters Part I (Cefn Coed and Vaynor Local History Society).

T.J. Harris. A Topographical Anthology of the Parish of Vaynor Prior to 1900 (Cefn Coed and Vaynor Local History Society).

J.O. Evans. The Cefn Coed Schools 1861-1956 (Cefn Coed and Vaynor Local History Society).

H.N. Savory. Brycheiniog Vol XV – Prehistoric Brecknock.

W. Morgan. The Illustrated Handbook of Vaynor.

V.J. Parry. Brecon and Merthyr Railway.

Ron. Gethin. Merthyr Rugby Football Club. 1876-1976.

Herbert Williams. Stage Coaches in Wales.

T.W. Burke and others. "Excavations at Pant Sychpant Penderyn, Brecs". Bulletin of Celtic Studies Vol XXII 1968.

D. Webley. Bulletin of the Board of Celtic Studies XVII (1956) and XVIII (1958).

Part Three: Natural History

MARY GILLHAM

The Infant Tâf Fawr

Heading west from the Tommy Jones obelisk on the great north scarp which towers above Llyn Cwm Llwch the northern branch of the Tâf Fawr will be intercepted. Follow the river downstream to a steep-sided cwm leading to a sheltered gorge. The contrast between the bleak moorland vegetation of the source area, and what can best be called the "hanging gardens" of the gorge is astounding, emphasising the importance of escaping grazing animals and biting winds to achieve full growth potential.

The Taff is notorious for its flash floods and the northern watershed goes far to explain why. Here is no peat bog soaking up the mountain rains and letting them go gently in a steady flow. Deluges fall on bald rock or sheep-grazed soil baked hard in summer and razed by wind in winter.

Such peat as occurs is drying and disintegrating to leave sharp-edged peat hags 1-3 feet high, for the climate is no longer cold enough nor wet enough for peat to continue to build up as it once did. However, what remains preserves a record of former plant communities for plant historians to study.

The cotton grass of the deep peats is replaced by sheep's fescue on the shallow soils exposed by erosion and this in its turn by wiry mat grass *(Nardus stricta)* as livestock nibbles the finer grass down to the bare land beneath. This is not a truly indigenous alpine grassland but a third community arising from loss of peat followed by overgrazing.

Sheets of water slide over the shorn grass after rain, dividing around clumps of deer sedge *(Trichophorum caespitosum)* and purple moor grass, *(Molinia caerulea)* flooding dor beetles and hunting spiders from their burrows. However, for most of the time the peat runnels are dry. Only a few pools remain permanently full, their water stained as brown as the peat itself. Plants need sunlight and shun the peaty infusion water, but some of the silt-floored pools lower down are half choked with the massed red stems of bulbous rush. Though often isolated, these pools are sufficiently permanent to contain fish fry.

Water beetles and water boatmen rise to tuck shining air bubbles under the tips of their wing cases to carry below. Whirligig beetles spend much time on the surface, their silvery sheen being of wax rather than trapped air. Red damselflies *(Pyrrhosoma nymphula)* emerge from these plateau pools and sometimes meet death by drowning if the nymph can find no emergent stem to crawl up at the crucial time. More splendid are the golden-ringed dragonflies *(Cordulegaster boltoni)* which hover over the pools, patrol the narrow watercourse and zoom away over the grassy-clad valley sides in search of flying prey. Common aeshna dragonflies (*Aeshna juncea)* also thrive in these acid pools, mature males resplendent in blue, with golden leading edges to their rattling wings, young males and females yellow or green. If their predatory nymphs avoid being eaten by brook trout for the 2 or more years needed to achieve adulthood, the expectancy of life of these superb fliers is a mere month.

The permanent watercourse

At intervals the recognisable stream is replaced by a belt of soft rush *Juncus effusus* var. *congestus)*; its eventual permanence owed to the regulating influence of marginal quagmires. *Sphagnum* moss helps more than any in retaining water but even this can lose its grip and change from apple green to cottony white as water in the honeycomb of cells is replaced by air. The species with lax green frond is *Sphagnum recurvum,* the chunkier browner one is *S. auriculatum.* Other mosses of these flushes are *Hypnum cuspidatum* and *Bryum pseudotriquetrum.*

Round-leaved sundews in the bog moss, spread glistening tentacles to trap unwary insects. Bog asphodel leaves, like mini-iris plants, herald yellow flower spikes, and delicate pink bells of bog pimpernel border floating rafts of bog pondweed. Tassels of narrow-leaved bog-cotton and mopheads of hare's-tail cotton grass shimmer when the sun shines, water starwort and water crowfoot take root among three-angled shoots of the water moss, *Fontinalis antipyretica.*

The eastern head-water of the Tâf Fawr is more precipitous than the northern. Narrow water-falls are draped with mosses and liverworts, which form a rooting medium for golden saxifrage and grey sallows which grow outward and downward before curving up to the light. A ruined stone building at the confluence supports mossy saxifrage on its crumbling walls and shelters a nettlebed in the rushy paddock where small heath butterflies come to feed.

The united stream tumbles down rapids and lingers in pools, where the flowers of marsh violet and New Zealand willow herb are often submerged during freshets. There are six-inch brown trout in the pools and yellow frogs in the slack water areas. Gerris pond skaters feed by sensing the ripples which midges generate on the water surface. Adult pond-skaters have learned to lift the prey above the surface to eliminate tell-tale ripples and keep their prizes to themselves!

Caddis larvae may cover the rocks in slack water areas with a lacy pattern of tapering tubes. These are of silk coated with silt grains and too fragile to withstand the scouring of more rapid flows. The inmates graze the encrusting algae which make the stones so slippery and grow best where the water is enriched with sheep dung. Midsummer clusters of caddis eggs are tinged green by minute algae living on the jelly.

Net-spinning caddis larvae occur only in fast stretches where the bag-shaped nets slung between stones to catch waterborne prey, trap silt particles as well, and look more substantial than they are. Those more familiar caddis larvae which drag their homes round with them live in all kinds of habitats. Tubes can be cylindrical or tapered, and of plant or pebble fragments or a mixture of both. Those made entirely of plant material are difficult to hold down in turbulent conditions, where heavier material is more useful. The abundant *Agapetis* larvae of vigorous stretches, cement their tubes of tiny red pebbles to the rocks for added security.

The Gorge and its "Hanging Gardens"

On the vertical faces of the Tâf Fawr small gorge plants benefit further from the mutual shelter afforded by cliffs. The constant, gentle trickles, year in year out, nourish roots that are short of soil and enable plants to survive on open rock faces. Lime, released as the calcareous inclusions dissolved from the cornstones of the Old Red Sandstone, helps to counteract acidity and make life possible for eyebright, fairy flax and bird's-foot trefoil.

Drapes of golden saxifrage are the first to cascade into flower as the icy fingers of winter withdraw. Primrose and yellow pimpernel, lady's-smock and wood sorrel, red campion and bugle, flourish in a woodland microhabitat. Whereas in the lowlands they need the shade, shelter and humidity of a tree canopy, here in the gorge air turbulence is stilled and humidity is high.

Unkempt Bilberry and heather reach inwards from a line of leaning rowans and silk tufts of greater woodrush rise from mats of their own dead leaves. Flowers star the leaf cushions of mossy saxifrage; meadowsweet, golden rod, angelica and mountain bitter vetch flower in July and August. Yellow hawkweed *(Hieracium* section *tridentula)* with purple-blotched leaves reaches from fleabane carpets, and 2 feet high fescue heads can scarcely be equated with the plants of the closely-nibbled fescue sward above. Ragged robin is succeeded by devil's bit and water mint in summer.

Where soil is sparse more modest plants such as lesser skullcap with pink trumpet flowers, and common, marsh and New Zealand willow herbs can reach the light. Butterwort unfurls insect-catching leaves. Purple thyme spills over dry brinks and herb Robert pokes from stone heaps between bog stitchwort and creeping pearlwort.

60 species of flowering plants occur in the "hanging gardens" − 6 times as many as on an equivalent area of the adjacent moorland. Yet the main asset of such habitats in the rainy western hills is the fern and bryophyte flora.

Delicate brittle bladder fern, wiry maidenhair spleenwort and robust tufts of hard fern and hard shield fern are characteristic, with both types of polypody fern, *Polypodium vulgare* and *P. interjectum.* Pea-green beech ferns form loose swards; crinkly-edged lady ferns, splaying tufts, while male fern and broad buckler venture from their usual woodland environment. *Minium punctatum,* its circular leaves transparent as dewdrops, is more like a liverwort than a moss and surpasses in delicacy the red-tinged *Scapania undulata* with which it grows. Frilly-edged fronds of *Pellia epiphylla* have a purple tint, while *Marchantia polymorpha* are covered with scallop-edged gemmae cups full of green reproductive discs or gemmae.

Although sheep and rabbits seldom enter the gorge in summer, by late July a whole family of 7-8 stoats may be seen skipping back and forth across the valley.

Their playful antics fill the resident meadow pipits with alarm. Their ground-dwelling chicks are an easy mouthful for a stoat, as are those of the grey wagtails nesting on little ledges of low cliffs. Fortunately, stoats hunt mainly by scent and nestling birds emit very little. Rabbits and denizens of many mouse-sized holes in the riverside herbage are more likely prey.

In winter stoats can hunt quite successfully in tunnels under the snow, catching prey which is invisible to the foxes padding across the white wastes above. Mice and voles feed more easily under snow than rabbits and hares which must dig.

Birds and the Valley at Pont ar Dâf

Magpies also prey on passerines nesting by the infant Taff, sometimes adjourning to a line of fenceposts to hold the prey under a foot, for ease of tearing off pieces. Ravens start breeding in the frigid months of February or March. A pair of nests here have been in use since 1969, unruly piles of sticks with sheep's wool lining. The nests are within a few yards of each other on the western cliff.

Common sorrel grows extra well by one of the nests; it excels itself when there is guano to be had. An excreta-splashed nettle patch has sprung up under the ravens' habitual perch and also in another which receives phosphate-rich drainage waters from the first patch.

Buzzards and kestrels nest in cliff face trees in this and adjacent valleys, sparrow hawks leave sad little piles of feathers at their plucking posts and merlins are occasionally seen. In spite of their way with rabbits, buzzards are mild of temper, allowing carrion crows to molest them for long spells. Although traditionally hunters, their 2½ inch long crop pellets may also reveal raspberry pips and fragments of beetle wing cases. The incongruity of an old buzzard picking raspberries is in keeping with the fact that all birds of prey will take fruit when it is in season, just as foxes will feed on blackberries and fallen apples, and there are plenty of wild raspberry canes in the woods hereabouts.

90　Kestrel with young. Hovering is the most distinctive feature of this bird of prey.

Keri Williams

89　Buzzard with young. This bird of prey is often seen soaring to great heights.

Keri Williams

91   Ring Ouzels and Whimberries.

The cliffs are ideal for ring ouzels, which are rare on this side of the Beacons where slopes are gentler and suitable crags in short supply. Nests made of straw are built at the base of haws and ash, bulging untidily outside but neatly lined within. Sallow and bilberry thickets echo with the ouzel's distinctive song which starts in March. Two broods may have been reared by July when family parties explore the heathery faces for insects and rowan berries, fanning out over the moor later on to gather bilberries and the few odd crowberries. Ring ouzels do not breed further south than the headwaters; others in the valley will be on passage.

Dippers are commoner and strongly territorial. Some stake possession of the tributaries, where they fix big mossy nests alongside the waterfalls. Each dip of the body when perched is accompanied by blinking, the startlingly white nictitating membrane clearly visible as it flicks across the eyeball. It is closed when the bird is under water. Wrens make similar shaped nests, often under a crumbling overhang of soil held by tree roots. They forage through the "hanging gardens" and by the stream.

Meadow pipits nesting among riverside grass tufts become less territorial when the young fledge. Wheatears are more closely tied to the sheep-grazed turf beyond, as their mode of foraging is ineffective in long grass, but their white rumps can be seen flashing through the gorge on occasion.

Star, oval, carnation and green-ribbed sedges crowd among rushes where the river broadens at Pont ar Dâf while smaller flea and common yellow sedge encroach among water blinks and *Philonotis fontana* moss. Water forget-me-not *(Myosotis secunda),* lesser spearwort, greater bird's-foot trefoil and white clover occupy quagmires. Lousewort creeps into less sodden areas, then milkwort, self heal and finally heath bedstraw and tormentil. On rocky outcrops where it is drier still wild strawberry, heath violet and sheep's sorrel occur.

Large black slugs *(Arion ater)* enjoy the wetter areas where sawfly larvae feed on the stems of soft rush. With only small internal shells, they need very

92   Dipper and butterwort.

little calcium and are commoner than snails in these lime-deficient uplands. Froth-blowing froghopper or cuckoospit nymphs *(Philaenus spumarius)* are at home anywhere, drawing their moisture from the plants on which they live. The little muscid fly, *Chirosia parvicornis,* lays eggs in fern tips, the resulting larvae burrowing into the green tissue to cause distortion and coiling of the developing fronds.

Below the stepping stones where the main Pen-y-Fan path crosses, the steep-sided tributaries are dominated by purple moor grass. Coltsfoot occurs on the clay banks in the col towards Storey Arms, orange *Hygrophorus* and *Hypholoma* toadstools on the turf, and parasols of *Panaeolus rickenii* on ripening pony dung.

Flowers and Birds of the Conifer Plantations

Prior to the recent acquisition by the National Trust, conifers were planted at Pont ar Dâf. Sheep-proof fencing round the little trees in the 60s and 70s had a profound effect on the moorland plants within. Wavy hair grass resembled a field of oats in June, silky, purplish heads swaying in the mountain breeze. It covered as much ground outside the fence but grew flush with the soil and scarcely flowered. Sheep's fescue, sweet vernal, Yorkshire fog and Timothy grasses benefited similarly. Trefoils, buttercups and tormentil flowered generously. A few hawthorns survived from before planting and oaks sprang up marginally. Hemp nettles, foxgloves and mouse-ear hawkweed add colour to the plot of mixed evergreens and larches. The pinewood of drier slopes above is coloured by heather, a species nibbled almost to extinction outside the fence. This is a perfect example of "fenceline ecology" but its span is limited. Plant successions move on unless held at an all-time low by some devastating factor such as overgrazing. Trees grow up to exclude the light and lesser plants disappear.

The cone-strewn ground under mature sitka spruce by the Beacons Reservoir is almost devoid of green. Bilberry and wavy hair grass survive in clearings, otherwise bent grass, heath bedstraw, wood sorrel and hard fern are the only four living under the trees. But the cycle goes full term. Some of the spruces are felled, as they reach marketable size. With the sunlight come the plant opportunists, supplied from seeds produced on the broad sward of ungrazed land left alongside the river.

The changing forest habitat dictates a succession of birds as well as of plants. Grasshopper warblers are only present among seedling trees; willow warblers stay longer. While the woodland matures, coal tits can nest in mouseholes in the ground; other tits need holes in trees, and conifers seldom reach this stage before being cut down. Blue and great tits are usually excluded, along with nuthatches and pied flycatchers, but the odd surviving birch or rowan may fill their need.

Redstarts and wheatears overcome the nesting problem by using holes in walls. Goldcrests sling their nest cradle on conifer twigs and there is lichen in plenty as nest material for long-tailed tits. Common hedgerow birds (blackbird, robin, dunnock, song thrush and chaffinch) find shelter in the young plantations. Mistle thrushes usually nest in the forks of bigger trees by the reservoir, and produce an amplified version of the grasshopper warbler's trilling. The ubiquitous magpies are joined by wood pigeons and jays, which are excessively noisy when the young are making their first exploratory sorties from the nest. Kingfishers are seen to sample the yellow-striped minnows of the placid stretch of river entering the lake.

Mature spruces were felled at the head of Llwyn-On Reservoir during the 1975 and 1976 breeding seasons, destroying the largest of Glamorgan's four heronries. 20-24 pairs of grey herons formerly nested in this part of the designated nature reserve, starting as early as February and continuing into July. Invisible treetop nests could be located by gutteral grunts and squawks; blue eggshells could be found below from the end of March and the odd gawky, half feathered young fell from a nest during April or May.

As waders, the herons' hunting is restricted to the water's edge, where they catch frogs and eels rather than the more elusive trout and pose little competition for anglers, although often more successful. They have their own way of dealing with slimy contaminants from the prey. The preen gland provides oil, as in other birds, but they are also equipped with powder down, a sort of home-produced talcum powder from the abrading tips of special feathers. There are two pairs of powder down patches on rump and breast in all herons, but our species has additional ones in the central shoulder region and above and behind each thigh. The middle toe is furnished with a comb to help in ablutions.

A less strident noise could sometimes be heard from a tawny owl's roost, marked by a collection of regurgitated crop pellets quite different from the long fishy ones of the herons. Dissection of these owl pellets and the piecing together of the intact skulls, jaws, hip girdles and limbs of mice, voles and shrews is a handy way of identifying the small mammals of the area without having to trap them. The remains of several score rodents could be found at a single gathering.

A kingfisher has a nest-hole in the river bank at the west end of the wood and dippers sometimes hunt over the boulders below. Tree creepers scour the spruce trunks for insects, a hunting terrain which they share with nuthatches, formerly rare here. Resounding calls of green and greater spotted woodpeckers echo round the plantation.

Grey squirrels pluck the dangling spruce cones and leave their gnawed centres on the old stumps used as dining tables. Big cones of Colorado spruce which lodge point downwards in the leaf litter are nibbled as they stand, on one side only, by small rodents. These will also have a go at the snails, biting off the top of the spire and hauling the animal from its shell, leaving the largest, lowest coil undamaged and not shattered like those found by song thrushes' anvils.

Old tree stumps harbour wasps' nests, the gentles or grubs prized by fishermen. *Bulgaria inquinans* sprouts rubbery black sporing bodies from fallen oaks where slugs lay spherical eggs like little pearls in crannies of the bark. Pink-spored *Pluteus cervinus* grows on oak roots where dor beetles carry colonies of little beige mites which are not parasites, but feed on excreta clinging to their dung-burrowing hosts. Non-biting fungus gnats emerge from maggots tunnelling in the flesh of scarlet-cap or sickener toadstools *(Russula emetica)* and their yellow counterparts, *Russula ochroleuca.*

Stinkhorn fungi *(Phallus impudicus)* open in profusion, exuding a dark green mucous to attract flies, which move off loaded with spores to spread the distinctive and only temporarily evil-smelling fungus yet further. Lawyer's wigs or shaggy caps *(Coprinus comatus)* also disperse their spores in a liquid matrix, allowing them to drip down with the 'ink' into which the gills disintegrate at maturity.

Boletus parasiticus, with a honeycomb of pores instead of gills, parasitise earth balls *(Scleroderma vulgare);* fairy caps *(Panaeolus rickenii)* sprout from pony dung. Fairy cake mushrooms *(Heboloma crustuliniforme)* smell of radishes; *Clitocybe suav eolens* of aniseed and *Mycena alcalina* of alkali.

Elliptical flanges of *Panus torulosa* fan from rowan trunks like smaller 'oysters of the woods', horsehair mushrooms *(Marasmius androsaceus)* sprout from fallen pine cones. The red and white fly agarics of the fairy tale books *(Amanita muscaria)* appear under birches; greasy brown *Collybia butyracea* under oaks and fleshy pink blushers *(Amanita rubescens)* romp away under spruces in almost complete darkness.

The Tributaries of the Tâf Fawr
Ffynnon Cwm Llysiog: The Valley of the healing well

On the barren moorland above the source of the Llysiog at about 1600 feet, small ponds are surrounded by grey sallows 6 feet hight, and there are also eared sallows *(Salix aurita)*. There are probably no other sallows within a mile and these, like the local soft rush, must depend heavily on the minerals bubbling from underground in this wilderness of peat. Rushes form a swathe along the stream; *Sphagnum,* which is less dependent on minerals, climbs the banks to occupy depressions watered by rain rather than springs in the bog above.

At a confluence between two moss-grown falls on the 1500 foot contour the stream bed is covered by an orange film of iron hydroxide precipitated out by iron bacteria.

More iron emerges in the other branch of Nant Llysiog coming from a higher source at Pont Garreg. This is the Ffynnon Llysiog (See page 41) which has cut a 12 foot gorge into deep peat. The stream here has the colour of black treacle and is innocent of plant life apart from a little *Cladonia* lichen and moss. The catchment is occupied by an acre or so of dark heather, contrasting with the pallid moor grass of the rest and dependent on the better drainage arising from the scoring of the whole block by a dendritic system of gullies.

Peat releases water sequentially, seldom drying out completely. In cold spells ridges of frozen peat form little weirs reminiscent of periglacial brooks flowing over permafrost. All around are eroded peat hags, often with pools around their base. The shoulder of land between Nant Llysiog and Nant Wern Ddu which joins it lower down has eroded free of peat in parts, the exposed soil supporting only mat grass and dwarf bilberry.

Nant Wern Ddu, after cutting deeply into the peat, plunges down a high waterfall into a steep-sided valley zig-zagging round interlocking spurs. There are sufficient minerals to nurture patches of rush, many flattened by the December 1979 floods with clods of peat and soil on top brought by lateral run-off on a broad front. Collapsed banks divert the flow at intervals.

Underground water may freeze and heave rocks of up to 18 inches diameter out through the turf to form long lines of slightly sloping screes but the movement is sufficiently gradual for colonisation by lichens.

Pools below a small stepped waterfall may be home to trout, which normally head up current in order to stay in the same place and intercept food items floating down. Such pools have an invertebrate fauna similar to fast stretches of stream, the animals mostly flattened for crawling out of the current under stones or furnished with a means of clinging on. Here are stoneflies and mayflies, shrimps and midges, net-spinning and tube-building caddis. Quieter pools harbour newts and frogs, water beetles and water boatmen, pond skaters and surface spiders. Common alongside are yellow-spotted green tiger beetles, orange-striped black sexton beetles and furry oak-eggar caterpillars.

Fox dung, vole runs and mole hills tell of mammal activity. Buzzards nest in a pine top, their bluish-white eggs visible from the slope above on a nest-lining of sheep's wool. The youngsters supplicate for food long after they are flying free. Scribbled brown eggs of grey wagtails hatch under grass overhangs, along with those of pied wagtails, and dippers which return to the same sites year after year.

Wheatears build further back among the frost-heaved stones, skylarks and meadow pipits in rough tussocks. Tree creepers, wrens, chaffinches and willow warblers sing from the line of birches; house martins forage over the stream and tree pipits perform their descending song flight in the lower valley.

Vegetation diversifies with loss of altitude to include ivy-leaved bellflower, and downy mildew *(Erisyphe)* encircles the stems and distorts the leaves of the New Zealand willow herb. Early hair grass flowers as late as July, when its lowland counterparts are long dead, their seeds scattered for an earlier spring awakening.

The valley narrows again towards the road and vegetation closes in, alder, hazel and birch separating a lush streamside community from encroaching conifers.

Nant Car

Nant Car flowing into Llwyn-On is unremarkable but typical of Old Red Sandstone tributaries in less rugged parts of the Brecon Beacons and it was proposed early on as a fitting addition to the Llwyn-On Nature Reserve. It flows from open moorland into sheep-dominated broad-leaved woodland backed by blocks of conifers. The main wood is very wet and dominated by alder, with durmast oak, rowan and ash and a wealth of epiphytes on trunks and branches. Haw, hazel and sallow may be shaggy with lichens, tufts of 'old man's beard' *(Usnea)* and frilly plates of *Parmelia.* Bluebell, red campion, woodland loosestrife and wood sorrel flower in clearings.

Pearl-bordered and small pearl-bordered fritillaries lay their eggs on violet leaves, green hairstreaks on bilberry and bramble where they eat flowers and fruits rather than leaves. Green-veined whites and orange-tips sip nectar from lady's-smock and wood bitter cress, and small heaths flutter in from the moor. Honeysuckle emits its finest perfume after dark to attract night-flying moths to pollinate the slender trumpet flowers, which can be serviced only by tongues as long as theirs. Syrphid hover-flies and drone flies can sup only from shallow floral cups such as those of marsh valerian and golden saxifrage.

The sequence of mossy falls and dripping cliffs is ideal for mosses (bryophytes), large numbers of which have been identified. Liverworts creeping over wet rocks above trout pools include slabby *Conocephalum conicum* and delicate *Lophocolea cuspidata.* Mosses such as *Hyocomium flagellare, Plagiothecium undulatum* and *P. denticulatum* grow by seepages. River limpets speckle the rocks, sharing the available shell-building material with the snails. (Wood sanicle, wild strawberry and *Cotoneaster* nearby suggest that lime may be present on a more generous scale than usual).

On humid evenings in June and July the air can be full of flying caddis and midges dancing in sun-rays slanting through the trees to appear as myriad golden flecks. Caddis flies are golden in any light, their wings covered with bright hairs analagous to the scales on the wings of moths. Discarded pupal skins of midges can be netted from the surface and relative numbers of the different species are used by experts to determine the water quality and suitability for stocking with different kinds of fish. The pupa sticks to the surface film and the adult climbs out, researchers sometimes able to gather as many as 2000 of 35 separate species in a few minutes.

Garw Nant

The Forestry Commission's picnic site and information centre at the north-west corner of the lowest reservoir on the lower course of Garw Nant opened in the summer of 1976.

Both branches of the stream arise in *Molinia* grassland. Firebreaks ploughed alongside the bordering conifer plots have become colonised by bent-fescue turf. Being more palatable than the moorland grasses, this is closely nibbled by sheep and thus rendered more effective.

The steep-sided valley profile of the southern branch is lined with sapling sallows; the northern branch meanders through *Sphagnum* with fewer woody species. Some big oaks and other broad-leaves have been spared, affording a welcome break of spring green and autumn gold which is reflected in the upper larches. In 1976 there was a glut of rowan berries, hazel nuts, haws, acorns and beech mast.

A lively tributary spreads out through a distinctive community of tussock sedge with scattered stools of tufted hair grass. Wood sorrel grows on the tumps, the leaves folding together in 'sleep movements' in wet weather as they do at night. Its delicate foliage (a candidate, with clovers, for the Irish shamrock) has a sharp acid taste and has been used as a garnish for salads. Primroses grow at the water's edge, away from nibbling sheep, their flowers submerged after rain. Lesser celandines are mostly higher up with common sorrel and sheep's sorrel, which two also have acid foliage.

Dead sedge stems can be speckled with pink, white-rimmed discs of sedge cup fungus, *(Sclerotinia sulcata).* These short-stalked apothecia or spore-bearing bodies sprout in April from ribbed black sclerotia formed of massed fungal threads embedded in the sedge stalks where they have been maturing through the winter. Spores from the pink 'elf cups' infect young flowering shoots which flop earthwards and fail to produce seeds.

Black ants *(Lasius niger)* are able to extend into this waterlogged community by building their nests high in the tussocks above flood level. Further up they build in moor-grass tussocks, making normal anthills only in drier areas, where most become moss-covered, the close cap of *Polytrichum juniperinum* covered with starry male heads and spiky capsules in early spring.

Garw Nant is a haunt of green hairstreak butterflies and the rarer white letter hairstreak has also been seen. Clouded yellows abounded in the 'clouded yellow year' of the early 1960s but none were recorded here during the influxes to Britain of 1976 and 1981. Humming bird hawk moths sometimes turn up.

Dr. John Etherington surveyed the freshwater life of Garw Nant in 1967 and found 3 genera of mayflies, 3 of stoneflies and 3 of caddis flies. The commonest mayflies were *Baetis,* mainly *B. rhodani;* others were *Ecdyonurus* and *Rhithrogena.* Most frequent of the stoneflies was *Amphinemura sulciollis;* others were *Leuctra,* mainly *L. inermis* and *Perlodids.* Caddis larvae included species of *Hydropsyche, Rhyacophila* and others which eluded identification. Freshwater shrimps ride pick-a-back and are preyed on by nymphs of damselflies and dragonflies.

Conifers bordering the picnic site and carpark did not grow at the plantation edge so are disfigured by dead branches almost to the apex where lateral growths were starved of light in the mutual press. Growth is apical, so the brittle brashings are destined to remain unhidden by new sprouts.

The Cwm Tâf Reservoirs

Around the reservoirs low temperatures and strong winds prevent warming of the surface water, so plankton grows only sparsely and the rest of the food chain is accordingly impoverished. Any warmth which is achieved during calm spells is lost when the water is over-turned by strong winds.

The exceptional Summer drought of 1976 provided unrivalled opportunity to examine the reservoir beds, with their drowned roads, bridges and walls, and to view aquatic communities which rarely break surface. Water plants are often better at surviving these drastic changes of circumstance than are animals. While they responded to the water shortage by producing tight bunches of leathery leaves to replace the long flowing ones of the submerged phase, water snails were dying in great numbers. By July and August 1976 the hardening mud was thickly speckled with the empty shells of wandering snails *(Lymnaea peregra),* while fish and water insects stranded in shrinking pools were easy prey for scavenging birds. Ponies and sheep, chief predators on the plants, were excluded at that time by iron railings, so vegetation had a reprieve and time to adapt.

Mountain lakes are generally poor in nutrients, and a paucity of mineral nutrients implies a paucity of floating plankton and bottom-living benthos which depends largely on a rain of edible matter from above. This leads inevitably to a reduction in the animal life which is dependent on these early links in the food chain – and a corresponding decrease in the fish and waterfowl which come to feed on them. However, water engineers appreciate the lack of growths which might clog their grids and sluices.

D.N. Johnson made a study of wildfowl in South Wales in 1973-74 and came up with some interesting differences between their upland and lowland feeding environments. He found an average of only 40 parts per million (ppm) of dissolved solids in the three Cwm Tâf reservoirs as opposed to 227 in Lisvane Reservoir near Cardiff. Alkalinity (as bicarbonate) was 11 ppm in Cwm Tâf and 158 at Lisvane. Dissolved calcium was 22 ppm instead of 136: dissolved magnesium between 3 and 11 instead of the 57 to 77 found at Cardiff (Lisvane and Roath Lake).

Even silica was down to 1 ppm as opposed to 6 or 9, in spite of the siliceous nature of the Cwm Tâf rocks. Ammonia was as little as 1/85 of the Lisvane reading, nitrate about ½ and nitrite so little as to be indeterminable.

Phosphate deficiency is limiting to plant growth if the level drops below 0.05 ppm. In Llwyn-On it hovers at this critical level: in the Beacons and Cantref it is lower (0.04 ppm) or ¼ the amount present in Lisvane. So we have in the reservoirs soft water, more or less neutral in reaction and poor in the basic minerals necessary for the growth of a vigorous wildlife.

Lake Bed Vegetation in the Upper Reservoirs

Wave action is most severe in Winter, when the reservoirs are usually full, so its scouring effect is manifested as a belt of bare pebbles just below high water mark. Silt is able to settle out further down.

Shoreweed *(Littorella lacustris)* is the first to tackle life among the uncompromising stones. It is well-named in both Latin and English, being both littoral (of the shore) and lacustrine (of the lake). In wet Summers it remains submerged, with cylindrical leaves long and erect. In dry Summers it shrinks into insignificance, but only then can it flower. As the air-bloated underwater leaves wilt and die, they are replaced in the rosette centre by small flat ones. Male flowers are borne on little stalks, sometimes no longer than the flimsy stamens; female flowers and the nutlets which follow are hidden among the leaf bases. As the stony shore gets drier the shoreweed rosettes get smaller so that every size of plant occurs from ½ inch dwarfs at the top to 8 inch giants in the water.

By late July at the Beacons Reservoir the ridge of shoreweed-covered mud connecting the spruce island with the western shore is liberally peppered with primrose yellow stamens. By mid October at Cantref Reservoir the 60 yard wide belt of shoreweed along the western shallows is spangled with the

151

autumnal yellow and bronze of birch, sallow and oak leaves. Parallel drift-lines snake across a sward, tinged sapphire with the fronds of *Riccia cavernosa,* its furrowed tips sparkling with spongy air chambers. This tiny liverwort is rare in Britain but also turned up in dune slacks at Margam in 1980. Shoreweed is strictly a pioneer, colonising stony terrain and thickening to a 100% ground cover when sand and gravel accumulate, but losing out in competition with more demanding species as silt thickens.

A leggy form of lesser spearwort is often the first to join it, stems straggling for several feet, rooting at intervals and flowering well on into December. Later there may be only flexuous, spoon-shaped seedling leaves rising from the lake-bed, a juvenile foliage which will persist into summer if the water level stays high. Fiorin and flote grass creep in at this stage with needle-leaved tufts of bristle club-rush. Undulating narrow-leaved pondweed and pink-flowered water purslane occupy deeper levels.

Stems of alternate-flowered water milfoil form a veritable underwater trout forest in winter but are left stranded on the mud in summer, to be replaced by short shoots with tough little leaves of the same plumose shape but more drought resistant. Water crowfoot follows suit and the two species of water starwort are only mini versions of their aquatic forms. Plants cannot move away from a worsening habitat as animals can, but water plants respond to potential catastrophe with a remarkable aptitude.

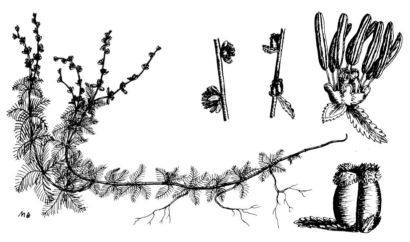

93 Alternate-flowered water milfoil. Insets: Top: Male flowers, Female Flowers, Hermaphrodite flower. Bottom: Female flower.

The Reservoirs in times of drought

Loss of water from Llwyn-On Reservoir in 1976, by evaporation as well as domestic and industrial use, exposed much of the skeleton of the pre-1925 valley. Yet, after deluges in September, the reservoirs were brimming over.

The soft muds of July were patterned by the prints of wagtails, sandpipers, coots, moorhens and herons. Plants unable to adapt had died, but many acres were covered with seedlings, some of opportunist land plants, others of regenerating water plants.

The old road undulated across three alluvial ridges reaching into the lake at the drowned village of Ynys-y-Felin. These had lost their tips by erosion, and the ends of their ridges fell abruptly to a water level of 20 feet below the winter norm. Fifty years after drowning the village was occupied by eight parallel bands of water plants. At the top the extended ground flora of the marginal sprucewood was invaded by marsh thistle. Next below was a belt of soft rush with cleavers, crosswort and lesser stitchwort from the land, meadow sweet, marsh willow herb and greater bird's foot trefoil from the water.

Zone 3 was dominated by common club-rush *(Eleocharis palustris)*, zone 4 by corn mint. Zone 5 was a bright green belt of shoreweed, the land form in full flower, with water crowfoot in gullies, water pepper on crumbling wall tops and amphibious bistort downshore. Zone 6 was also of shoreweed, but composed of the brown and dying leaves of the aquatic phase. Moribund creeping yellow cress was being replaced by exuberant seedlings. In zone 7, millions more seedlings pushed up among deflated water milfoil. Lowermost and remaining partly submerged throughout, were finely dissected fronds of the big green alga, stonewort *(Nitella flexilis)* with starwort and water milfoil.

Other parts of the shore showed concentric bands of marsh cudweed, each a little taller than the one below, the uppermost fruiting as the lowermost pushed from the seed coat. This little annual must produce enormous quantities of seed, to await, perhaps for several years, the onset of propitious conditions for germination. Plantains, self heal and others from the land must also behave as annuals, hurrying through a much briefer life span than that enjoyed by their kind upshore.

The Headwater Marshes

The river deposits silt where the flow is checked on entering each reservoir. Small scale marshes and deltas result. These headwater marshes are the most fertile part of the system, where green blanket weed is nourished by minerals from upstream.

Wind-blown rows of underwater plants torn free by wave action and drifted ashore, add to the fertility; e.g. fronds of *Fontinalis* drying to a crisp black in summer but fading to moist yellow in rainy spells. Terrestrial and aquatic mosses mingle among upshore club-rush. A strange, permanently juvenile form of bog pondweed *(Potamogeton polygonifolius)* with delicate, elongated foliage grows in the upper reservoir. Articulated stems of water horsetail, almost bereft of branches, pierce its rafts of leaves or sprout from the marsh pennywort discs of more organic rich soils.

Some species from the richer lowlands have established themselves in these favoured corners of the uplands but such as greater water plantain grow but half the size of their contemporaries in southern canals, while water pepper obviously misses the farmyard manure of its habitual field pond sites. Towards the top of the marsh is bluish bottle or break sedge, then short reed canary grass, with kingcup, lady's-smock, marsh bedstraw, angelica and gipsywort.

At the Beacons Reservoir there may be more white marsh thistle than purple. At Cantref Reservoir marsh foxtail is one of the dominants and thyme-leaved speedwell invades the toad-rush turf. At Llwyn-On reservoir earthy stools of tussock sedge dot the marsh. These may be chomped off 2 feet from the ground now that animals have access behind the railings, and consist mainly of a fibrous organic column impregnated with roots. Co-habiting with these are oval sedge, marsh valerian, meadowsweet and silverweed.

Water Fowl

Poor in nutrients, the Cwm Tâf reservoirs attract few water fowl. Dabbling ducks are particularly poorly served as they need rich shallows in which to upend and most of the shores are stony. They feed round the headwater marshes but rest in the greater safety of the open water. The 100 or so mallard winter at Llwyn-On. A few stay to breed along with coot and moorhen.

Teal and wigeon are infrequent, and shoveler rare. Mallard are 'general purpose' feeders, while teal are mainly filter feeders. Wigeon are grazers but prefer the sweeter grasses of the lowlands. Pochard and tufted duck are the most constant of the diving ducks, winter flocks reaching 60 to 80, but goldeneye are the most notable and are usually about in the colder months in groups of 4 or 5. They dive as readily among waves as in calm water.

Deep water presents fewer problems to goldeneye than to other divers and the study by D.N.Johnson showed that they descend habitually to 32 feet, stay below for up to 46 seconds and travel up to 50 yards under water at a calculated speed of 6 feet per second.

They will forage for an hour or two before stopping for a 4 minute preen, combing their essential waterproofing methodically from tail to head. A brief flap, to settle the feathers to rights, and they are off again for more feeding. Freshwater shrimps, midge and caddis larvae, water bugs, water snails, fish fry and seeds make up their diet, so they are mainly non-vegetarian.

Goosanders, also expert divers, turn up occasionally, feeding mainly on the minnow population which shares the waters with the trout, and there are a few scaup, pintail and long-tailed duck. The odd smew may be seen at the southern reservoirs between November and April.

Canada geese drop in occasionally and there may be mute swans, but the whooper swans from the Arctic are more evocative of wild places. In early April these winterers may overlap with breeding activity among the locals, dozing in groups while one keeps watch.

Whoopers arrive about November and shuttle constantly between the various reservoirs, sometimes as many as 16 together, but usually fewer. They are still about when the great crested grebes start the bobbing, dipping and shuffling of their courtship dances. Sometimes there are two pairs of grebes on Llwyn-On, where they attempt to breed most years but seldom succeed because of the fluctuating levels due to water usage. They can be seen through most of the non-breeding season except in cold spells, when they retreat South.

Little grebes probably breed successfully: Slavonian grebes, like great northern divers, are unusual passage migrants. Cormorants and shelduck sometimes fly up river from the sea, some 30 miles away, to sample the fare offered by the mountain waters. Cormorants have been regular Winter visitors since before 1882, when the river flowed unhindered by dams.

Coot are probably the most numerous of the water birds, building up to 200 plus in Winter. For reasons known only to themselves, gulls do not congregate here as in the Tâf Fechan Valley, although the odd few, including common gulls from the North, visit spasmodically.

Common sandpipers are the most familiar waders, one or two pairs usually nesting by each reservoir, bobbing their tails on the shingle beaches alongside the aptly named wagtails, grey and pied. Green sandpipers, wood sandpipers, greenshanks and oyster-catchers pay fleeting visits, but the lack of shallows mitigates against wading birds.

Snipe are usually away in the mountain bogs, and Brecon's only dotterel nest was recorded well South of its usual range, at Pen Moel Allt west of Llwyn On. Unlikely birds were the red phalarope picked up dead near Cantref Reservoir in September 1950 and the Leach's fork-tailed petrel found dead in October 1952.

Ospreys appear more frequently, having become regular passage migrants during the past decade. In 1979 one was around for 3 weeks during February and March, a noble visitor which could not be grudged his small quota of trout by the most ardent angler.

In pursuit of smaller prey are the swifts, swallows and martins which arrive soon after mid April, flying low over the water in windy weather, but soaring to great heights to feed on high-flying insects in the warmer weather.

Animals of Lake and Lakeside

Helping to keep insect numbers down are the frogs and toads. Both are plentiful, the former a week or so ahead of the latter in their breeding, but later than their lowland counterparts. Falling water level in early April can

94 Minnows in the May breeding season. Female left, male right.

leave innumerable slabs of frogspawn stranded on the headwater marshes, their moribund jelly green with unicellular algae and 'nailed' to the ground by sprouting rods of water horsetail. Such casualties must curtail the population severely some years; other casualties are due to predation. Remains of pregnant females carried back among the conifers to be eaten include tight-packed masses of unlaid, unexpanded spawn wisely discarded with the skeleton. These masses would have swelled up when moistened by digestive juices and could have spelt disaster for the hunter.

Toads may be found in tandem, at mating time, dry-skinned, among marginal sedges or under a foot of water, even in the fast flow where the river enters. Put ashore or into the water, pairs will return to the medium of their choice without losing their grip.

The Cwm Tâf Reservoirs do not have the coarse fish, perch and pike, of the Tâf Fechan ones – only brown and rainbow trout, minnows and other minutiae. Trout retreat to deep water, 40 feet or so offshore in cold or rough weather, when there is no fly 'hatch', as they do if much worried by anglers. Ideal conditions for the emergence of flies from the aquatic pupal phase are calm weather, with no wind or rain to disperse them once they are through the surface film – the tension of which is such that weaklings may not make it, but die of drowning! Their temperature requirements are modest and the lower air can be full of gnats and midges on quite cold days in early spring. Many are scooped from the water surface by gyrating whirligig beetles, which will also dive for morsels below. These versatile creatures enjoy the best of both worlds, their eyes divided amidships to enable them good vision both above and below water. The bubble of air which they tuck under the shining wing cases when they dive, makes them so buoyant that they have to keep going or hang on, to avoid bobbing back to the surface. Middle and hind legs are modified into short, broad paddles, made broader by their fringe of hairs; the front pair is used as arms, for grasping prey.

Creatures pleasant and unpleasant emerge from the lake waters. Where tributaries tumble in, golden-ringed dragonflies and demoiselle agrions (sometimes referred to as kingfisher demoiselles for their beauty) scoop up more of the gnats and help to reduce the population of biting midges and

156

clegs or horseflies. Blue leaf hoppers *(Cicadella viridis)* move down to the lower shoreweed zone as the waters recede and spiders follow the retreating shoreline, sprinting out across the water itself on calm days, to extend their hunting territory into that of the water striders.

One of the most prolific animal habitats is the tussock sedge community at Llwyn On, where predator and prey live side by side around the sides of the tall, damp stools. The soil is recessed half way down under the dead leaves, erosion during the wet phase hastened by vole runs excavated during the dry. Already, by late May, the grassy nests of field voles can be found tucked in earthy hollows skirted by the crown of leaves and constructed in the faith that there will be no more submergence until after the breeding season.

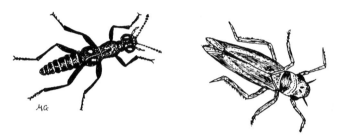

95　Small Rove beetle, *Stenus biguttatus*, and Leaf hopper, *Cicadella viridis*.

Narrow-bodied rove beetles with a red spot on each of the short wing cases, *Stenus biguttatus,* wriggle through the mesh of rootlets, with shining black carabid beetles. Centipedes dining on the latter, bite the head off first, then the legs, before eating the rest. Millipedes and woodlice are resident vegetarians.

Even in early Spring, the abundance of spiders, wolf spiders and web-spinners, scuttling over the tussocks implies an abundance of prey, which must increase enormously during the Summer breeding season. Scarlet mites creep round the sedge tops, orange slugs round their bases. Copse snails *(Arianta arbustorum)* and white-lipped hedge snails *(Cepaea hortensis)* tuck themselves into crannies between browsing expeditions under cover of darkness or on rainy days. Both have quite delicate shells compared with their kind elsewhere, like the myriad snails of the lake-beds. With so little lime available for shell building, it is surprising that there are as many as there are.

Limestone and grit areas of the Tâf Fawr

Limestone crags rise steeply to the east of Tâf Fawr, with the A470 cutting across the screes. On the west the profile is more complicated, and wooded with ash and hazel. Downstream, the slopes support oakwood. Oaks are less expert at wrapping their roots round naked boulder and prising open cracks to insert woody anchors than are ashes, but they can suppress ash once established, by their denser shade.

A stream rising north of the small quarry has deposited tufa where its speed is checked by the old quarry tram track – a ready source of lime for mosses like *Cratoneuron commutatum*, which become progressively crustier with age, until completely petrified. Small-leaved lime and field maple grow with rowan, sycamore, elder and field rose. The wild garlic, sweet woodruff and wild strawberry beneath would not be there without the lime, but the primroses, bluebells and wood anemones are less choosy. Sanicle and mountain pea on river pebbles grade down to coltsfoot and butterbur, which are submerged during spates. There are a few cowslips about, and low-growers, like spring whitlow grass and thyme, confined to anthills.

Hard shield fern almost completely replaces the commoner male fern, others are as expected, with the delicate brittle bladder fern geared to these northern latitudes, and absent from South Glamorgan. Feathery swards of oak fern and beach fern are an uncommon and attractive feature. Ferns like rusty-back are lime-lovers, hard fern an acid-lover.

Tâf Fawr was once an otter stream and is clean enough to be so again. There are brown and rainbow trout for the taking, bullheads and minnow shoals to be chased. No polecats have been recorded but stoats and weasels are common and there is a badger sett above the dramroad. Fresh droppings in the badgers' dung pits can be full of iridescent beetle remains but no quantitative estimate can be made because earthworms, often the commonest food item, leave few recognisable remains.

This steep fragment of woodland formed a last refuge for red squirrels, once abundant and lingering until 1966. Greys are now everywhere, leaving split nutshells, gnawed acorns and disembowelled haw stones on fence posts, mossy boulders and rotting stumps. Bank voles and wood mice also open up haws, discarding most of the yellow flesh and boring into the stones. Hares occur on the plateau above, rabbits on the plain below and there are occasional sightings of fox, hedgehog, mole, shrew and lizard.

The varied habitats in close juxtaposition are reflected in the bird life. There are buzzards, kestrels, and ravens from the crags; dippers, kingfishers, wagtails and mallard by the river. A pair of merlins recently hatched 3 young just up the valley quite close to a populous carpark. Flocks of fieldfares (but few redwings) join the crows, jackdaws and wood pigeons on the flood plain in winter; bramblings join the chaffinches, yellow-hammers and woodpeckers in the wood.

With spring comes the repetitive call of the cuckoo and there are redstarts about, though pied flycatchers, so often associated with them in the oakwoods of Mid-Wales, have not been seen. Wood warblers, willow warblers and whitethroats are summer residents, but chiff-chaffs pass through, not staying to breed. Nor is the enclosed landscape suited to whinchat or wheatear, which prefer open hillsides.

96 Kingfisher. A fast flight and a flash of brilliant blue is sometimes seen along the rivers and streams.   *Keri Williams*

Penmoelallt Woodland Nature Reserve and the rare whitebeams

Penmoelallt Wood is on a lee face and sheltered from the westerlies. The predominance of ash over oak where the rock ledges are exposed, gives a distinctive type of woodland with yew, lime, purging buckthorn, dogwood, beech, wych elm, field maple, crabapple, bird cherry and bullace *(Prunus institia)*.

Specialists are the whitebeams, a group of trees confined to chalk and limestone and likely to throw up local, true-breeding ecotypes which have been granted the status of full species. Commonest here is the rock whitebeam *(Sorbus rupicola)*, identified by Michael Porter, botanical recorder for Breconshire. It occurs in other sites, in both Wales and England.

Its toothed leaves resemble a mealy white version of the wych elm; its fruits are the rich red of the common whitebeam *(S. aria)* of the south.

Sorbus porrigentiformis, probably also here, has leaves longer, narrower and pointed. It also accurs at Craig-y-Cilau further east in the National Park which is the only known site of *S. minima.* The Rev. Augustin Ley discovered this species and also the highlight of Cwm Tâf, which was named Ley's whitebeam or *S. leyana* in his honour by Alfred Wilmott – himself the discoverer of *S. wilmottiana,* endemic to the Avon Gorge at Bristol. Ley's whitebeam grows on both sides of Cwm Tâf in its brief passage through the limestone, but nowhere else in the world. Richard Mabey in *'The Common Ground',* ·1980, points out that Ley's whitebeam is Britain's rarest plant internationally, with a world population of about a dozen trees! To be custodians of such a species is a responsibility, the first and most important phase of conservation achieved by Peter Walters-Davies of the Nature Conservancy and Jack Evans of the Merthyr Naturalists' when they persuaded the Forestry Commission not to clear-fell and replant the whole area!

Seeds germinate unwillingly. Experimentally they have been found to need six months in a freezer, then a month's thaw followed by another month of freezing before the embryo finally breaks free, and this combination of circumstances cannot often obtain in nature. Jack Evans, who discovered the Penmoelallt 'colony' of four trees, in the late 1950s, persuaded the Forestry Commission to germinate some of the seeds. The resulting young plants, fenced off from sheep, rooted and flourished. By the Autumn of 1971 they had reached to ten feet and produced a few fruits.

The two parent plants were of particular interest as being the first true trees of the species known to science and reaching forty feet high. The original discovery, on the opposite flank of the valley, was of stunted shrubs, too windswept to attain their full and unsuspected potential. Clapham, Tutin and Warburg in the standard *'Flora of the British Isles',* 1954, describe the new endemic as "a shrub, 2m. high".

97   Ley's Whitebeam, *Sorbus leyana.*

98 Penmoelallt Forest Nature Reserve. Conifer trees are now growing above the
hardwoods.   *Jack Evans*

Some of the leaves of Ley's whitebeam are wavy-edged, like those of wild
service. There are yet others in the Beacons National Park. *S. leptophylla*
occurs in two areas in Brecon, *S. anglica* in Brecon, the Wye Valley and
Montgomery. The genus *Sorbus* includes the rowan *(S. aucuparia)* and the
wild service *(S. torminalis)*.

There are three main groups. The first, with simple leaves and closest to
the common whitebeam *(Sorbus aria* agg. (or aggregate)) includes *S. porrigentiformis*. The second, which is intermediate between rowan and
whitebeam *(S. intermedia* agg.), includes *S. leyana*. The third, lying between
whitebeam and wild service *(S. latifolia* agg.), includes *S. bristoliensis,*
confined to Avon Gorge across the Channel.

Lily of the Valley *(Convalleria majalis)* has persisted since 1890, but
remains confined to a single ledge 10′ x 2′, with no evidence of viable seeds
from the scarlet berries. False oxlips turn up most years and other spring
flowers are moschatel, yellow archangel, 3-nerved sandwort and early wood
violet, followed by early purple orchid, twayblade, cuckoopint and greater
stitchwort. Harebell, devil's bit scabious, betony and enchanter's nightshade
come into flower as the spectacular carpets of ramsons fade.

Rarest of all locally is the mountain melick *(Melica nutans)* known
otherwise in Glamorgan only as an ancient record on the limestones of
Morlais Hill. The single row of spikelets does not turn the rich chestnut of
the accompanying wood melick, which occurs here with black bent *(Agrostis
gigantea)* and hairy brome *(Bromus ramosus)*.

Nant Sychbant and the Moors above the Penmoelallt Nature Reserve

A conifer plantation encircles the 1,376 feet summit of Onllwyn, reaching from the southern boundary of the National Park to the Sychbant River. There, lodgepole pine sends orange roots through the top few inches of soil above badly-gleyed, waterlogged clays. Larch occupies better, deeper soils, with marginal bent-fescue instead of moor grass and heather. Others are Western hemlock, Norway spruce and a close belt of sycamores.

Before afforestation there was a fine grouse moor on the plateau, preserved by the English ironmasters, who were also instrumental in conserving the scree woodland (as cover for gamebirds) but other trees for miles around the busy iron foundries were being felled to make charcoal for the smelters. There are stone butts, still, on the top, where the guns crouched while the beaters sent the birds towards them, at least until the 1930s. Servants brought al fresco meals, to be eaten often by the limestone sink to the west.

Bilberry and heather afforded food and shelter and the bag included red grouse, black grouse, pheasant and partridge. Red grouse still enjoy the fruit of the more than usually abundant black crowberry, but their alternative favourite, cranberry, is rare here. Other foods are whimberries, young heather shoots, clover and sorrel leaves, while ants and other insects are collected for their chicks.

Organised shooting parties entailed keepering and management, with rotational burning to keep the heather from getting leggy. Light sheep grazing achieves the latter, but shooting is now by 'cowboys' from the Valleys who put nothing into the system and the stocks are dwindling. Pheasant and partridge are seldom seen, but black game, with their predilection for young conifer shoots as food, have increased since the coming of forestry.

Several pairs of nightjars used to nest here, the whole hillside full of their churring calls in summer dusks. It was not forestry which spelled their doom; they had started to dwindle before the second world war, along with the nightingales, which are remembered in local place names. Both species are rare now in South Wales. It is a more mundane bird which may excite the imagination of today's hill walker; not by its rarity but by sheer weight of numbers. A massive starling roost was found in August 1979, just south of the main swallow hole. 30,000 – 40,000 birds assemble here at twilight, gathering first on the grass and then adjourning in parties to the edge of the wood with the usual mob hysteria before they finally settle. Siskins and goldcrests are coming into the plantations. Green woodpeckers swoop out across the moor to probe the anthills and jays screech intermittently from bordering trees.

Globe flowers occur westwards towards Penderyn, their almost equally rare associates, meadow plume thistle and greater burnet, occurring with lady's mantle and kingcups by the Sychbant. A variety of ferns grows on the Ogof Fawr cliffs by one of the swallow holes close to the opposite extreme of bog vegetation with insectivorous sundew and butterwort, bog asphodel and cotton grass. Three special plants of the stream are marsh St. Johns wort, bog bean and marsh arrow grass, with lousewort, bog pimpernel and ivy-leaved bell-flower alongside.

Humbler species include algal wefts of *Hormidium* on damp forestry tracks and the moss, *Dichodontium pellucidum* in wet runnels. On the acid grey grit moorland are *Diplophyllum albicans, Dicranella heteromall, Polytrichum urnigerum* and *Hypnum cupressiforme* var. *ericetorum.* The Mesolithic hut circles are covered with *Pleurozium schreberi, Dicranum scoparium, Rhytidiadelphus squarrosus* and *Hypnum cupressiforme* var. *cupressiforme.* and the lichens *Cladonia impexa, C. pyxidata, Parmelia tubulosa* and *P. saxatilis.*

The apalling non-summer of 1974 was disastrous for butterflies but by October the heather was alive with the bristly caterpillars of oak-eggar moths *(Lasiocampus quercuscallunae)* looking for somewhere to pupate. Other 'woolly bears' were fox moths *(Macrothylacia rubi),* feeding on bilberry, heather and bramble preparatory to hibernating – as cater-pillars, not chrysalids. Limestone grassland yielded broom moth caterpillars *(Ceramica pisi)* which ate bracken here, in the absence of broom. They come in two colour forms, the longitudinal yellow stripes on either a green or a deep brown background, but only the dark form has been seen here. Magpie moths *(Abraxus grossulariae),* their larvae the same orange, black and white warning colouration as the winged insects, feed on the blackthorn, hawthorn and wild currant of the woods.

Ffrwd Millstone Grit Areas: Cwm Ffrwd

Botanically the valley is an enigma. It starts prosaically enough at about 1250 feet as two broad shallow valleys carved into the grit moorland south of the Onllwyn limestone. The vegetation is of moor plants growing on glacial clays among quartz conglomerate boulders. Where it plunges into the steep descent from 1000 to 700 feet at the level of the Cefn Coed stone viaduct, the vegetation becomes lime loving, although the rocks remain unchanged.

Lime-rich water seeping from the cliffs permeates the leaf mould to nurture drifts of wild garlic, which cannot grow without lime. Much is precipitated out on the cliffs with the help of creeping mosses to form bosses of tufa with tutsan, dogwood and wild clematis, which also need the extra minerals. This tufa is more apparent on the north side of the gorge, the limey waters percolating along the southward dipping strata, and forming masses of tufa.

The gorge is deep and narrow where the Heads of the Valleys road crosses and two spectacular falls occur where bands of hard grit interrupt the flow.

It is possible to sit on a ledge behind a curtain of spray some 20 feet above the plunge pool of the upper one. Primroses bloom here, in a constant rain of spray, but in a hard winter the whole system congeals into what must be one of the finest icicle curtains in the national park.

Giant horsetail, great woodrush, cat's valerian and meadowsweet with a few globe flowers occupy quagmires at the cliff base among commoner marsh plants like brooklime, hemlock water dropwort, water blinks and bog stitchwort. Guelder rose and goat sallow cling to cliffs and the abbreviated Welsh form of hard shield fern *(Polystichum aculueatum* var. *cambricum)* sprouts from crevices alongside the ordinary form. The ground flora savours of neutral rather than acid woods, carpets of dog's mercury pierced by the creamy cowls of wild arum, with bush vetch and honeysuckle. Fleshy toothwort grows parasitic on roots of hazel and elm.

On the grassy shoulder well above stream level are mountain pea, lady's mantle, betony and spring sedge *(Carex caryophyllea)*. Wood anemone, and lesser woodrush *(Luzula pilosa)* flower in the open − a relic woodland flora persisting without shade for 35 years since the overarching trees were felled. Birds are particularly abundant.

Limestone Cliffs of the Eastern Valleyside

Steep rock faces, mobile scree and westerly aspect have kept the plant succession at an early stage on the eastern valleyside. Incongruously, there is much gorse along the roadside, a species unusual on limestone, otherwise the community is lime loving with good diversity and several rarities. Much has been designated as a Site of Special Scientific Interest by the Nature Conservancy Council; the northern part held as a nature reserve by the Merthyr and District Naturalists' Society, the southern part by the Brecon Trust for Nature Conservation.

Grazing is largely responsible for the general treelessness. Ox-eye and polypody flourish on a rock column standing clear of the cliff edge but a sheep track, marked by a strip of yellow-green annual meadow grass,

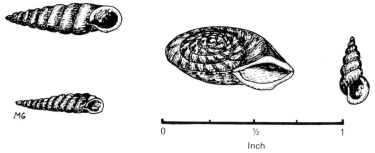

99 Four limestone snails. Left: Plaited door snail (top), Two-toothed door snail (bottom). Mid: Lapidary snail. Right: Lesser bullin.

follows the cliff brink and sheep reaching down lop the tops of the trees below, even the reputedly poisonous yews. Sheltering grounds of sheep at the foot of the cliff are marked by nettles, burdock, Buxbaum's speedwell and self heal. Woodland, mostly on the lower northern slopes, is of sycamore on deep soil, ash on shallow, with lime, buckthorn and the rare whitebeams mainly towards the south. It grades north through haw scrub, slashed or browsed back at intervals and with lichens on quite young twigs indicating a slow growth rate.

Haw leaf margins may become rolled into crimson galls by a rare aphid, *Rhopalosiphum crataegullum*. Galls are local, scattered and often in shade. Woodland flowers are much as on the opposite, ungrazed valley flank, the pungent garlic leaves apparently disliked and left alone by stock. An interesting addition is the rare narrow-leaved bitter cress *(Cardamine impatiens)*.

Open cliffs are notable for their mossy saxifrage and lesser meadow rue *(Thalictrum minus)*, which flowers at 18 inches high on inaccessible faces but remains short on scree, being bitten off flush as it tops the stones. Three aromatic dead nettles are marjoram, wild basil and wild thyme growing with hawkweeds, golden rod and bird's foot trefoil. Mosses include *Grimmia pulvinata, Tortella tortuosa* and *Tortula intermedia*. Flat shoots of *Fissidens cristatus* grow in crevices, and the mountain liverwort, *Preissia quadrata* sprouts little four-sided sporting umbrellas where water drips onto ledges.

Shaded rock faces support shining cranesbill; the related Herb Robert is more often on screes. Ivy is common to both, sometimes permeating a scree, which it helps to stabilise, while not appearing above the surface. Others on scree are flat meadow grass *(poacompressa)* and a blue-grey form of sheep's fescue. Much scree is covered in limestone polypody *(Gymnocarpium robertianum)* and the almost equally rare green spleenwort. The mountain sedge *(Carex montana)*, also very localised, occurs with bluish glaucous sedge and yellowish common sedge *(Carex nigra)*.

Limestone grassland is quite distinctive with its rock rose, salad burnet, bulbous buttercup, harebell, carline thistle, heath grass, oat grass, crosswort and lady's bedstraw. Rare members of this last genus identified here are false cleavers *(Galium spurium)* and small heath bedstraw *(G. sterneri)*. The elusive adder's tongue fern is to be found among chestnut-spined puffballs *(Lycoperdon echinatum)* and gnomes' cap *Hygrophores conicus*.

There is a rich animal life, with occasionally a merlin breeding at the top, badgers halfway down. Two snails found only on the higher scarp are the plaited door snail *(Marpessa laminata)*, which resembles a fallen beech bud and is uncommon this far west, and the lapidary snail *(Helicogona lapicida)*, confined in Wales to the eastern counties. Two species to be found throughout are the two-toothed door snail *(Clausilia bidentatus)* and the lesser bullin *(Ena obscura)*.

Millstone grit moorland of Cil Sanws

Sheep's fescue is the only plant common on both green outcrops and brown peaty infills of this moorland. On the first it is associated with bent and heath grasses, field daisy, yellow trefoils and eyebright *(Euphrasia nemorosa);* on the second with moor, mat, tufted hair and wavy hair grasses, deer sedge and tormentil. Green-ribbed sedge *(Carex binervis)* is confined to the peat with Koch's rush, sundew and asphodel. Sheep much prefer the limestone turf, though cropping the young shoots of western gorse, and there are unusual juxtapositions of thyme and bilberry where the contrasting communities abut.

Ice-scraped, quartz conglomerate boulders support *Rhizocarpon geographicum,* (with black 'maps' etched on green), various Cladonias and the shaggy mountain moss *(Rhacomitrium lanuginosum),* a world-wide species of mountain tops. Some of the swallets, where the millstone grit has collapsed into limestone cavities beneath, contain rushes, some have rocky sides colonised by heather, others have deeper soils with bracken, these favoured by resting sheep. Sheep also scrape out their own 'lairs', their dung stimulating arum and lesser celandine which escape the heaviest trampling by dying back to underground organs in winter. Chickweed passes the winter as seeds.

Tâf Fechan – Source and the Reservoirs

Headwaters of the Tâf Fechan

The southern flank of Pen-y-fan is deeply scored by the channels which coalesce to form the Tâf Fechan. The upper courses, fed only by surface run-off, are usually dry, but springs emerge lower down, some into quagmires where butterwort, sundew and bog pimpernel creep across the constantly wet *Sphagnum* moss.

Westwards the steep face of Gwaun Tâf merges into the precipitous crags of Craig Fan-ddu, where sea campion *(Silene maritima)* is to be found. Common on seashores, this is one of a trio of maritime plants which is occasionally pushed back to the marginal habitat of mountain tops as well as sea coasts. It is the commonest of the three in the Brecon Beacons, although confined to a few inaccessible faces. The other two are sea pink and sea plantain.

Eastwards the land rises more gently towards the old Roman road climbing Tor Glas to the summit ridge and cols. Massed glacial drift and solifluction 'head' dissected into lobes and snouts by the young river, are dominated by mat grass above and moor grass below. Their colours complement each other, the mat grass green in Winter and Spring, with purple flower stems turning to strawey seed spikes in late Summer; the moor grass bleached to a paler straw colour in Winter and Spring, the green of June heralding purplish flower heads in August. Livestock may crop the flowers from both when feed is short, confusing the visual 'distribution map'. There has been an increase of brood mares and colts on the hills to supply the expanding pony trekking centres, and lambing flocks are on the hills until the big sheep muster of September/October, when the yearlings are separated off for sale and the tegs returned to winter on the heights. Few woody plants survive their attentions, the chief subordinates among grass, rush and sedge being dwarf milkwort, lousewort, eyebright and tormentil. Lesser skullcap and spearwort, marsh pennywort and bedstraw grow in seepages, slender St. John's wort *(Hypericum pulchrum),* marsh hawksbeard *(Crepis paludosa)* and hawkweeds on craggy faces.

Once a haunt of peregrines, the source area of the Tâf Fechan is still a place where hen harriers can be seen. Fieldfares flock in hundreds to the lower slopes in Winter, sometimes with mistle thrushes or redwings, but avoid the windier tops. Sandpipers nest by streamside, as well as at the reservoirs, and local herons alight to feed on brook trout, frogs and stripe-winged grasshoppers. Wheatears and meadow pipits pick off hairy St. Mark's flies from the gyrating swarms and are themselves occasionally picked off by hawks, which are well able to outmanoeuvre them in the air.

In hard winters such as 1978 fabulous ice formations advance across golden saxifrage and water blinks. Sheep may be driven from snow-clad slopes as a precaution against worse to come.

Continuous ice may cover the still waters of the Upper Neuadd Reservoir, but this is seldom thick enough to support livestock, and the vegetation of the offshore island remained ungrazed before the 1976 drought. It supported self-regenerating woodland – indicative of what the whole of this bleak moorland might be in the absence of grazing. Scots pine occupied its low summit, with rowan and bushy heather in the under-storey; species grazed right out on most of the mainland. Young trees were scattered over the remainder of the island, mostly grey sallows, with downy birch and pine to 3 feet high, although this part is under water when the reservoir is full.

By early August of the drought year, sheep walking across the dry lakebed to the island had stripped all willow leaves within reach but left the pine saplings unscathed. Ponies had chomped the tops from larger bushes, leaving straggly remnants. The long term balance between grassland and woodland is obviously dependent on the regulation of water levels and stock access.

100 Common Sandpiper, a characteristic bird of the reservoirs and hill streams.
Keri Williams

The low levels of August 1976 exposed some 20 acres of the reservoir bed and this was found to be dominated by a very rare species, recorded in but a few sites in Brecon and Radnor and not at all in Glamorgan. This was needle spike rush *(Eleocharis acicularis)*.

Strictly a shoreline plant, the rush remains green and sterile while submerged, but had turned chestnut from its wispy covering of flowering and fruiting heads by August. Towards the lake margins the bed was occupied by shoreweed *(Littorella)*. This is another unable to reproduce sexually when submerged, but had flowered so exuberantly here that the nutlets were borne on ¼ inch stalks instead of being sessile in the leaf axils.

Both species spread by short runners, giving a mutually exclusive ground cover of leaf rosettes and the junction between the two communities was a mosaic of pure patches of each, with little minglings. Both are poor competitors, occupying unwanted acres. On the more fertile deposits of silt dumped at the lakehead the community diversified, with red-leaved water purslane, green water starwort and blue-grey marsh cudweed. Needle spike rush did not penetrate the deeper parts, which, after a gap between the two were occupied by narrow-leaved pondweed *(Potamogeton berchtoldii)*.

Angular stones predominate only near the Winter shoreline, where wave action is most prevalent. Water runnels cutting into the lake sediments below, showed these to consist of alternating layers of pale leached sand and dark peaty silt, depending on the size of particles brought in by spates. Shoreweed occupied the stony substances, needle spike rush the finer ones. Some of the silt dried and cracked into 'crazy paving' in 1976, but a line of springs was revealed, emerging from beneath a peat layer on the southern bed. Water close beneath the surface produced a quicksand effect in places.

Neuadd is the highest and least productive of all the reservoirs, lying at 1,506 feet in an 82 inch rainfall zone, with a poor mineral content and poor plant and animal life. Emergent vegetation is sparse, just a little water horsetail and bottle sedge, with common spike rush upshore. Littoral plants such as kingcup remain small, so low-growing ivy-leaved crowfoot, marsh

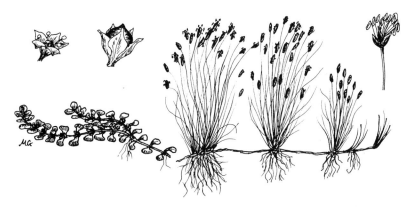

101   Water purslane and Needle-leaved spike rush.

violet and marsh pennywort can spread unhindered. Often nothing more than moss covers the thin skin of peat above the stones, with orange-tipped, white-stalked *Mitrula paludosa* fungi sprouting from sodden fir cones.

The efficient wind-dispersal of fluffy sallow seeds and winged pine seeds was ably demonstrated in August 1976 when a good scatter of seedlings occurred right across the lake bed. The young pines were 2 inches high, the young sallows 4 inches; all doomed to drown when the water returned in September.

Animals, too, had followed the water down and a 'Summer camp' of water vole burrows had been excavated along a section of stream which is normally 6-12 feet beneath the surface. Invertebrates, apart from the standard hordes of *Lymnaea* water snails, had tunnelled into the mud and the lakebed was criss-crossed by the tracks of foraging wagtails, sandpipers and herons.

Wildfowl come seldom. Even mallard are sparse, and the only others seen are teal, pochard and the occasional visiting swan. Wrens rummage among undermined tree roots at the Winter water level, cocks' nests spurned by the hens for breeding, serving as Winter roosts. Swallows nest in the tower on the dam, house martins under the eaves.

Big shoals of minnows were present during the drought, when both brown and rainbow trout were rising to snap at stranded winged ants which had swarmed to a watery death during their nuptial flight. In the early 1970s when Irish salmon disease was prevalent on Usk and Wye, footbaths were furnished for fishermen on the Tâf Reservoirs to prevent its introduction here — the chemical solution was of course fenced off from livestock.

Torpantau Woods and the Hills above

The Lower Neuadd Reservoir is much smaller than the Upper and hedged about with mature conifers which clothe most of the valley sides down to the Pontsticill Reservoir. More were planted in the upper valley in the 1970s.

There are several badger setts high on the surrounding hills, some of them shared by foxes. Examination of badger and fox scats shows that the food of the two is not dissimilar. Both contain elytra of violet ground beetles and dor beetles (as do crop pellets of the owls) and both animals will dig out nests of mice, voles and rabbits, but the badgers have a special liking for bluebell bulbs. Red squirrels were common here a quarter of a century ago and there was a five year overlap with the North American invaders. Now there are only greys. Occasional reports are received of pine martens in the high spruce plantations and conditions seem right for them to settle.

Siskins feed among alders, goldcrests among pines, but coal tits nesting in the ruinous walls show no preference here. Redstarts, wood warblers and spotted flycatchers prefer deciduous trees, and birds generally, like insects, are abundant in the sheltered cwms.

102 Nuthatch feeding young at nest-hole in tree.   *Keri Williams*

As the most southerly true mountains in Britain, the Brecon Beacons have yielded several Arctic-alpine species of insects not known South of Snowdonia until recently. One inhabiting the bald mountain between Torpantau and the Usk catchment is *Nebria nivalis*. This is a Carabid or ground beetle resembling the common black *Nebria brevicollis,* which is here too, and figures in the diet of the local foxes. Another is *Anthophagus caraboides,* a bright brown Staphylinid or 'cocktail' beetle and one of the few members of the group to live in trees. Its British centre of population is North Scotland.

Less notable but more noticeable are the scarlet cardinal beetles *(Pyrochroa coccinia),* often seen on the flowers of hawthorn and

171

umbellifers, and the green tiger beetles *(Cicindela campestris).* *Abax parallelopidus* is a savage black ground beetle likely to fall upon earwigs or other edible morsels and tear them to pieces. *Agriotes acuminatus* is one of two click beetles leaping more nimbly when flipped onto their backs than the smaller flea beetles and ground hoppers. Iridescent chafer or scarab beetles, *Aphodius fimetarius,* can be found in the nests of yellow ants, *Lasius flavus,* or under stones. Water beetles include the black, feathery-legged *Acilius sulcata* as well as the readily recognisable great diving beetle *(Dytiscus marginalis).*

The big stonefly species or Perlodids, notably *Perla cephalotes,* seem only to occur in these mountain streams, not penetrating the lowlands. In late May and early June streamside rocks can be speckled with hundreds of their nymphal skins, the emergent insects crawling around on the banks, seldom flying unless hard-pressed. Smaller green stoneflies *(Isoperla* sp.*)* and the brown *Nemoura variegata* fly readily and settle among the tree branches. Mature caddis flies also move into streamside trees, along with Tipulids or craneflies, including Britain's largest, *Tipula maxima.* Alder flies *(Sialis lutarius)* crawl from danger rather than taking wing. Communal nests of tree wasps *(Vespula sylvestris)* may be found dangling in undergrowth, and big predatory flies, hairy and with yellow legs and wings *(Empis tesselata)* appear in June, with Dolichopodids and other two-winged hunters.

Pearly everlasting *(Anaphalis margaritacea),* usually a 'follower of man' in more industrial areas, has colonised the old railway track near Torpantau Station, where spikey black peacock caterpillars and leaf hoppers *(Eupteryx urticae)* feed on nettle leaves. Small heath butterflies take nectar from lesser spearwort, and orange-tips lay their eggs on cuckoo flower stems.

The woods are full of fungi, one of the most unusual being the brown slime mould, *Leocarpus fragilis.* A rare and poisonous toadstool is *Inocybe patouillardii.* Green-flecked orange milk caps, *Lactarius deterrimus* grow under firs, red-flecked yellow *Trichomolopsis rutilans* round spruce stumps. There is *Boletus bovinus* with velvetty cap, the slimy *Boletus elegans*, and countless others.

Pentwyn Reservoir (Part of the Tâf Fechan Reservoir)

Pentwyn has the greatest biological turnover of the seven Taff reservoirs, its waters fairly hard, slightly alkaline and so shallow that they warm right through in Summer without any of the usual temperature stratification. Nevertheless, its 96 acres, with a maximum depth of 36 feet dwindled to nothing in the dry Summers of 1976 and 1977 when the stretch from the headwater marsh to the dam was heavily stocked with sheep and resembled green fields with the Tâf Fechan snaking across the centre.

Notwithstanding the sometimes elusive nature of their chosen medium, reservoir plants are more diverse than on any of the others, e.g. the bottle sedge and water bistort loaded with nutlets beloved by water fowl. Species here that are more often encountered in the low lands are yellow loosestrife and marsh foxtail, but the fertility-demanding greater water plantain cannot satisfy all its needs and often remains in the juvenile aquatic phase throughout the year.

Extensive flowering rafts of water crowfoot (probably *Ranunculus aquatilis* ssp. *radians)* beautify the Summer scene. Oddly these bear more circular floating leaves when in water than on land. Plants stranded on the mud continue to produce the finely dissected underwater type of foliage, but with shorter, chunkier segments. Only on stonier shores are growths low enough to include thyme-leaved speedwell and bristle spike rush.

Pentwyn is a designated nature reserve, frequented by ornithologists and fishermen, with sailing confined to the more barren Pontsticill Reservoir downstream. Unlike the Cwm Tâf and Neuadd Reservoirs, it contains roach and pike as well as brown and rainbow trout (neither occurring in the equally or more productive Tal-y-Bont across the watershed). An attempt to remove them to improve the trout fishing gave some idea of their numbers. A single operation led to the capture of 10,000 small roach. 20,000 roach fry, 1 pike and 1,000 trout, these estimated as a small proportion of the whole – which equates the Pentwyn roach with those of heavily populated parts of the Thames!

Roach are shoaling fish and attract goosanders (as they do on Llangorse and Llandegfedd to the East) but the shallowness of this reservoir makes fishing more profitable for these sawbill ducks. Otter sightings in recent decades are few and far between but are more likely to be here than by the other reservoirs. Polecats are recorded quite often.

The fluctuations in water level prove a serious problem to nesting water birds. During the bitter May and June of 1972 the reservoir was brimful, other years it may be almost dry by May. An area serving fifty swimming pochard one year can be supporting a couple of hundred standing gulls another year, at the same season.

Great crested grebes, four pairs of which may attempt to breed simult-aneously, are particularly affected. Carrion crows are more likely to attack eggs and chicks in a shorebound nest and chicks having to return to the nest across an expanse of open shore are very vulnerable, as, indeed, are adults, which have sacrificed much of their mobility on land to manoeuvrability in the water.

Divers are even more awkward onshore, and sightings of great-northern and black-throated divers, like those of whooper and bewick swans, are confined to Winter. Mallard, little grebe, coot and moorhen attempt to breed but are troubled by the changing levels. Winter wildfowl include teal, wigeon, shoveler, pochard, tufted duck, goldeneye, common scoter and the occasional ferruginous duck.

Herons occur up to 7 at a time and cormorants sometimes come this far up river to fish. The leach's fork-tailed petrel was part of a 'sea-bird wreck', but ospreys may fly this way and stay to feed. The reservoir is not a wader haunt, but 4 species nest round about; curlew, lapwing and snipe, as well as the inevitable sandpipers.

Trees and shrubs are plentiful at the upper end, in spite of felling of the mature plantation, and conditions are as sheltered for Summer birds as in the lowlands. Whitethroat, willow warbler, garden warbler, goldcrest, redstart, reed bunting and bullfinch occur. Tree-creepers leave the mature trees to forage on the spindly stems of sheep-pruned blackthorns, and chaffinches scoop Biblionid flies from the air — less methodically than the local experts in this technique, the spotted flycatchers. Mistle thrushes are among those moving uphill in August to feast on bilberries, returning to the rowan, haw and bramble of the valley woods to winter with nuthatch, woodpeckers and tits.

Pontsticill Reservoir, although largest of the seven, is too deep at 107 feet and too steep-sided for good populations of plants or wildfowl. More significantly, it has no headwater marsh, being separated from Pentwyn only by a low dam.

Withdrawal of domestic water exposes many acres of stony bed. In 1976, by 20th April the level was already 20 feet down, after the driest 11 months for 2 centuries — with the long Summer drought not yet begun. Plants are similar to those of Pentwyn but much sparser and the water crowfoot and creeping yellow cress, geared to the lower water regime, remain below the usual Summer water level, where silt settles out. The stony slopes above are dominated by field horsetail, silverweed and adventives from the land. Sheep have free access and probably account for the abundance of water pepper, which is protected from their attentions by its unpalatably acrid sap. The upper lakebed under the wave-cut notch of the dam is occupied by New Zealand willow herb.

A mixture of bordering coniferous and deciduous woodland, grassy patches and hedgebanks disappearing beneath the water, results in an incredibly rich fungus flora. Over 80 species were found in the snow of 26th November, 1978 — brought on by a fortnight's rain on the sun-warmed soils of a dry Autumn. Extra habitats are provided by shallow-rooted Norway spruces toppled in gales, many of them affected by pineapple or pseudocone galls induced by aphids *(Adelges abietes)*.

Roach and pike occur, as in Pentwyn, and mink were recorded in September 1977 in the south-west corner of the reservoir. Bats roost in the tunnel leading through the dam to the Tâf Fechan below, leaving a plaster of black guano on the walls. A dead cormorant picked up here in September 1974 had been ringed on St. Margaret's Island in Pembrokeshire. Waterfowl are seldom seen, but Pontsticill forms a regular roost for some 3,000 herring gulls which commute here nightly from the industrial valleys. There can be almost as many black-headed gulls and increasing numbers of lesser blackbacks are over-wintering of late. Greater black-backs can number up to 20 or so.

Cwm Callan and Cwm Car

Cwm Callan enters the Tâf Fechan from the East and supports shoaling minnows as well as roach, brook trout and probably loach and bullheads. Smooth newts occur with the commoner amphibians in the lower pool. Livestock trampling across the tributary runnels cause the banks to coalesce above the water in parts, giving strings of peat pans reminiscent of the similarly formed salt pans of estuarine flats. Unusual plants are cow wheat *(Melampyrum pratense)* and water avens *(Geum rivale)*.

Cwm Car entering Pontsticill Reservoir from the West forms the county boundary between Powys and Mid Glamorgan and is of particular interest for the transition to limestone organisms where it crosses the Neath Fault. Inhabitants of the ruined farmhouse on the southern edge of the limestone outlier got their water from a spring bubbling from the side of a badger hole, its bed speckled with stony caddis tubes, its waters full of shrimps. They burned lime hewn on one side of the fault to spread over land on the other. Today trees grow in the ruins, planted by the birds seeking shelter there.

Men no longer live on these hills, but they still run their flocks there and Nant Rhyddau is dammed back for sheep before being allowed to hurtle over the red cliff alongside the settlers' stream into the sandstone basin at Blaen Car. The lower fall spans some 30 feet and big trout lie in pools below cliffs shaggy with gorse, rowan and bilberry, unable to reach the streams above to feed alongside heron and dipper.

The shattered slopes below gorge and scree are wooded and the air sufficiently moist for lichens to establish on birch and alder when these are little more than saplings. Spotted orchids mingle with ragged robin in feathery stands of giant horsetail. Rare lesser tussock sedge *(Carex diandra)* grows with hairy sedge *(Carex hirta),* a commoner species, but more characteristic of south-eastern lowlands. Winter heliotrope and yellow cress penetrate to shingle banks of the lower stream from the western embankment of the reservoir.

Limestone Reaches of the Tâf Fechan

Grassy slopes and limestone pavement at Morlais and Vaynor

East of the Tâf Fechan, old quarries scar the upper face until the river bends away westwards, but Morlais Hill and the castle ruins provide excellent examples of undistinguished limestone pasture with a few of the cowslips indicative of old grassland. The turf is closely grazed bent-fescue with the expected rock-rose, salad-burnet and doves-foot, but also the unexpected mountain everlasting *(Antennaria dioica),* mountain sedge and mountain melick. Woodland relics (wild arum, dog's mercury, lesser celandine, early purple and twayblade orchids) persist in the scant shade of gnawed hazel and thorn bushes; mossy saxifrage and biting stonecrop cling to the walls of castle and moat above the golf course.

West of the river the land rises more gently and boulder clay has been retained on the spur east of Vaynor – this now occupied by small fields. Limestone pavement lies towards the summit, around the Pengelli Fach and Pengelli Fawr Farms but is little known because it is set back from the road and its vegetation has progressed to the final phase of ashwood, so that it does not show on aerial photographs like that at Ystradfellte (which is quoted as the most southerly in Wales).

Both the two lower sections have been colonised by ashwood, roots of the now mature trees wrapped closely about the blocks, pushing into the crevices and insinuating themselves along the bedding plane beneath, sometimes prising the blocks loose so that they can be levered off for use as walling stone. Herbs get established in mossy solution hollows, but crevices can be 3-4 feet deep so, unless lodged on the sides, and all seedlings but those with the biggest food supply get starved and etiolated before they can reach up to the light.

The ashes themselves can establish on the stone surfaces, as they do on ruined buildings, putting roots down the faces with all the facility of strangling fig trees. Roots of sycamore are also adept at enwrapping rocks in the lower woodland, with field maple – their leaves studded with red pimple galls induced by Eriophyid mites, *Macrorhynchus aceribus* and blotched with common tar spot fungus, *Rhytisma acerinum.* Beech, the main tree associate in the upper woodland block, lost its leaves prematurely in the 1976 drought, as an insurance against too great a water loss. Downy birch is also shallow-rooted and suffered at that time, but wych elms and oaks were scarcely affected.

The mossy covering of the woodland stone blocks was shrivelled to a brittle brown, but took no permanent harm and was lush and green again by early October. Herbs recuperated more slowly, the free-range dairy cattle having to browse on ash leaves that Autumn, but 80 odd species were recorded a few years later.

Above the woodland the crevices become progressively filled with blown dust and the trampling of livestock, and the 'pavement' grades into a partially bald hilltop with scarcely dissected limestone slabs. Crested dogstail and common bent dominate a short sward having much ribwort plantain, field daisy, salad burnet and clovers. Good King Henry, greater plantain and knot grass are confined to gateways, but the habitat is sufficiently open for sandworts, eyebrights and other miniature plants. Such little soil as is present is well turned by earthworms and, wherever depth allows, the moles which hunt them throw up their mounds alongside those of ants.

The Limestone Quarries

The rehabilitation of life in old quarries re-enacts the original colonisation as soil first began to build up. Cliff faces out of reach of grazing animals allow the succession to proceed beyond the stage attained on the surrounding hills and it is only here that shrubs and briars can reach full potential. The thick mats of cocksfoot, hairy oat and golden oat grass on ledges if similarly uninhibited on the flat, would destroy the essential character of the limestone flora by smothering the small and delicate plants. A bonus, however, among the thickets of wood-sage and hawksbeard *(Hieracium* sect. *glandulifera)* which grow quite out of reach is wood spurge *(Euphorbia amygdaloides)*.

It is in the Baltic Quarry, along the eastern valleyside, that the fluted, gelatinous, coral-red fungus, *Tremiscus helvelloides,* was first discovered on 27th September, 1973, softly cushioned in moss over sodden sleepers on the old tram track. New to Wales (and to England, too, 13 months before, apart from unsubstantiated records in 1891 and 1914), it turned up also at Tylerstown, Llanwonno and Aberpergwm that Autumn — on waste mine timber.

Present in Europe mainly in montane coniferous forest, there is an anomalous lowland population by the Baltic Sea — source of timber imported into South Wales by mining and quarrying companies for use in the Baltic Quarry, Baltic Sawmill and elsewhere. Un-accountably it remained in hiding for a very long time after its likely introduction. (See Glamorgan Naturalists' Trust Bulletin, 1974 for an account of its multiple arrival.)

Grassland established on the floor of the old Twynau Gwynion Quarry next to the South is bristly with stemless thistle *(Cirsium acaule)* — a plant of the English chalk which is uncommon in South Glamorgan and even more so this far North. Free drainage is the key to its survival in the high rainfall of what is, in essence, a peat-forming climate. With it are carline thistle, hairy hawkbit, fern-grass *(Catapodium rigidum)* and others of the downs, with pure stands of thyme over considerable areas.

Astonishingly large numbers of wrinkled snails *(Helicella caperata)* appear, particularly after rain. They are named for the ridges on their disproportionately thick chalky shells with central hole or umbilicus, a shell mostly white, often striped, sometimes dark and rarely orange. Dead plant material is the snails' favoured food and they often climb emergent stems to benefit from cooling breezes while feeding during the heat of the day. Spiders too are abundant and a wealth of 'chalkhill' butterflies.

Organic debris, dust, flower seeds and moss spores lodge in joints to form lines of growth on slabby rocks of the Morlais Quarry floor. In time a bronze mat of the moss, *Acrocladium cuspidatum* coalesces across the surface. This soaks up moisture and supports tiny field speedwell, field madder, parsley piert and spring whitlow grass early in the year, but dries out and peels away in rainless spells. Mossy saxifrage here, grows little larger than the associated rue-leaved saxifrage and was badly hit by the 1976 drought, taking many years to recover. Wild and barren strawberry, thyme-leaved and slender sandwort, lesser and hop trefoil and stonecrop are characteristic. So many of these small plants compete on even terms with mosses and liverworts, 109 species of the latter two being recorded.

Spoil tips 100 years old can be completely colonised or almost bare depending on the mobility of the spoil, but most plants are close-shaven by sheep, the rosettes of plantain, daisy, hawkbit and dovesfoot a product of their incessant trampling. Very small plants thrive here too, fairy flax, pale flowered milkwort, lady's bedstraw, eyebright and mouse-ear chickweeds. Those such as bird's-foot trefoil, crosswort and burnet saxifrage which straggle to 10-12 inches on cliff ledges seldom reach 2 inches here.

Vaynor Quarry on the opposite side of the valley is still being worked and is moving perilously near the Ogof-y-Ci cave system, in which occasional oil spillages have appeared. 20 year old spoil tips here are dominated by New Zealand willow herb, which is more often a plant of streamsides. Rosebay willow herb, coltsfoot and mouse-ear hawk-weed come in quite early and the infrequency of grazing in the bustle of quarrying encourages others.

Vaynor Churchyard with its overgrown Norman tower is a good place to study the ready-dated rate of plant colonisation on the different kinds of rock used for tombstones. From the nutritional point of view the limestones (more easily dissolved in lichen acids) are most favourable, but this is overridden by texture, the polished marbles providing fewer plant niches even than the slates except in the carved inscriptions. Guano boosts orange lichens on headstones used by perching birds and crop pellets lodged here have introduced seeds of ivy, briar and bramble.

Tawny owls nesting in the tower, roost in the hollow centres of ancient box clumps and among the lammas shoots of shaggy yews. Fruits of the last attract birds and mammals: fieldfares and redwings to feast on the fleshy pink arils, and tits and rodents break open the supposedly poisonous seeds for their nutty kernels. This is a site for a third saxifrage, the meadow species, *Saxifraga granulata.*

Mountain seepages and the river to Blue Pool (Pwll Glâs)

Spring water highly impregnated with lime, bubbles from below ground at intervals to deposit its load of minerals as cheesy, yellowish tufa. Water dribbling down cliffs gets colonised by blue-green algae, of forms ranging from brown slimy trails to dark jelly blobs. Fleshy crisp-edged *Riccardia pinguis* is one of the less usual liverworts.

Mineral-rich waters diffusing through the hill swards, nourish distinctive assemblages of plants which Dr. John Etherington regards as outliers of a residual post-glacial flora in areas which have remained open throughout the advance of forest since the last Ice Age. Some of the components – giant horsetail, dwarf mint, fleabane and quaking grass – are quite common; others are by no means so.

Rarest is the broad-leaved cotton-grass *(Eriophorum latifolium)* which, unlike the bog cottons, is a plant of neutral fen peats. With it are an unusual yellow sedge *(Carex lepidocarpa)*, marsh arrow-grass, square-stemmed St. John's-wort and devil's-bit scabious as well as the usual aquatics. Perhaps most surprising are the knotted pearlwort *(Sagina nodosa)*, so much more characteristic of dune slacks, and butterwort, more often in acid sites with the other insect-eating plants.

The broad river valley running South from Pontsticill narrows as it sweeps westward, the wooded flanks of Morlais Glen up to 200 feet high where the river carves its pot-holey way through the limestone to the viaduct at Pont Sarn. Although not included in the designated Nature Reserve, this is as fascinating a stretch as any. There is a double ox-bow upstream of the viaduct, the outermost abandoned meander at a higher level, lined with organic silt and full of golden kingcups in spring. The lower is still rock-floored, as when scoured by the brisk current.

Riverside plants include sneezewort *(Anchillea ptarmica)*, cat's valerian, marsh violet (the only acid-lover) and succulent-leaved marsh arrow grass, growing just offshore, out of reach of sheep, which produce a horizontal browse-line on the lower alder branches. Butterbur and reed canary grass are the chief island species, but sallow and alder seedlings can reach to nearly 2 feet high in the lee of boulders before getting washed away. More persistent ones may be epiphytised by wild gooseberries and currants *(Ribes uva-crispa* and *Ribes rubrum* or *sylvestre)*.

The river is too swift to encourage frogs to breed and most drop their spawn in stiller waters alongside, but the tadpoles of pools entered by subterranean springs get churned around with the shingle if they venture too near the water source. Life may be uncomfortable for these, but they are not in danger of drying out prematurely, like those of the quagmires, where temperature regime and food potential are quite different.

Any tadpoles living in the limestone potholes formed when the river flowed at a higher level are in imminent danger of desiccation in dry summers, but a thunderstorm of 4th July 1976 had washed well-grown tadpoles into a number of such potholes which had been waterless during the previous three weeks of temperatures in the 80s and 90s. Several of the larger puddles contained lime-encrusted fronds of stonewort *(Chara vulgaris)*, but in most, the only food source must have been the algae and fungi growing on sodden leaves.

Only more permanent pools, such as those on the hills towards Morlais Castle and Cil Sanws, support palmate and great crested newts, perch and tench. Roach and minnows occur also in the river with the trout.

Mallard lead their flotillas of ducklings to the river under cover of darkness and their nests can be found almost anywhere in the damp paddocks alongside, among soft rushes or under bracken. One was located on top of a "stoggle" – a naturally pollarded willow with branches splaying from a hollow, rotting top. Ducklings hatch well-developed and leave the nest only hours after chipping out of the eggshells.

Other occupants of tree hollows are tawny owls. Long-eared owls nest in the valley occasionally, as in 1972, and a hoopoe visited Pont Sarn in 1953. Kingfishers frequent the entire stretch, from the reservoir down, but were scarce for some years after the freeze-ups of 1946-47 and 1962-63, as were green woodpeckers. Greater spotted woodpeckers, happily, are increasing.

103   Green wood-pecker preparing a nest-hole   *Keri Williams*

The habitat is 'made' for dippers and grey wagtails, which exploit it to the full, and herons visit regularly. Jackdaws and ravens based on the quarry cliffs above come down to feed, but stick to the more open stretches. Song thrushes desert the higher woods in Winter, leaving these to the hardier mistle thrushes, which only retreat to the valleys in the most severe weather.

In late September 1979 a flock of blue and great tits was watched dangling from the leaves of sessile oaks to tweak the pea galls from the veins beneath. Only scarlet ones were taken. In the white ones the causative grubs would be undeveloped as yet (tits have demonstrated their known sensitivity to colour differences in their selection of milk bottle tops). Holding the gall on a branch with one foot, the tit would peck out the larva or pupa and let the fleshy part fall. Those pecking diligently at galls which they made no attempt to dislodge, were taking aphids from the surface.

Pea galls are formed by the unisexual generation of the Cynipid wasp, *Cynips divisa;* marble galls on the same trees are caused by the unisexual generation of another, *Andricus kollari.* These were still green and were left alone by the tits. Only later would the birds come to tap at the hard brown marbles to see if they were occupied, and dig them out. A third excrescence on these oaks was the bud-like artichoke gall caused by the unsexual generation of *Andricus fecundator.*

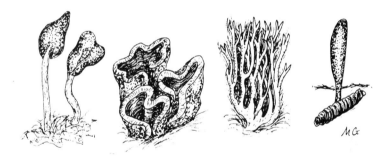

104   Four small fungi: Orange club, *Mitrula paludosa,* the rare red *Tremiscus helvelloides,* white Coral fungus, *Ramaria stricta* and scarlet Caterpillar club, *Cordyceps militaris.*

Three kinds of gall on nearby alder leaves are produced by Eriophyid mites. Commonest are the bubble galls scattered across the leaf surface and induced by *Eriophyes laevis-inangulis.* Bubbles produced along either side of the midrib are the work of *E. axillare;* multiple scattered blisters are formed by *E. brevitarsus.*

There were rare sightings of otters in the 1970s just below Pontsticill, where the bats hunt. A local rabbit-catcher's dog flushes polecats not infrequently, but is not yet known to have encountered a mink, these having moved in only recently. The dog will not risk following a polecat into a hole, and polecats caught in rabbit traps can inflict severe bites. Foxes are increasing but a lot of grey squirrels were found dead of unknown cause in 1979.

Nant Glais

Most of the headwaters of the Glais flow over peaty moorland, where they become charged with organic acids to help dissolve the limestone rock in the lower section, which is both a Nature Reserve and a Site of Special Scientific Interest. Calcium carbonate is eaten away to form potholes and redeposited to form tufa as the products of destruction of ancient rocks go to form modern ones. The dynamism with which the cliff east of Vaynor is currently eroding is shown by the three hedge-lines, each set a little further back into the fields as the cliff brink encroaches. These limey slopes have been farmed since Neolithic times and a count of woody species in the entwined remnants of the outermost hedge suggests that this is many centuries old.

In the stream's middle section there is a gorge with vertical cliffs of limestone above and below with slopes of looser material supporting scrub woodland. Water which surfaces in the stream is sufficiently pure and highly oxygenated to carry one of Britain's few freshwater red algae, *Lemanea fluviatile,* along with green tufts of *Cladophora* and two mosses of fast-flowing water, *Eurhynchium riparioides* and *Hygrohypnum palustre,* with wispy spore capsules. *Brachythecium rivulare* and *Dichodontium pellucidum* are others in the water, with crinkly-leaved *Ctenidium molluscum* and *Cratoneuron commutatum* on wet rocks above. The mosses clinging to the bases of stalactites severed when the roof collapsed include *Eucladium verticillatum,* which seldom fruits under natural conditions, but does so prolifically here. Two of the commonest mosses on the great tufa bosses plastered to the cliff faces are *Thamnium alopecurum* and *Fissidens cristatus.*

There are two caves in the valley. 45 species of animals have been recorded in the upper cave system of Ogof-y-Ci by Dr. G.T. Jefferson. Some of these are true Troglodites, which cannot live outside caves except briefly when washed out by floods. The tiny depigmented spider, *Porrhomma rosenhaueri,* is the most noteworthy, this being its only known site in mainland Britain until 1982, when it was discovered in the Little Garth Cave, where these same limestone beds surface South of the Coalfield a few miles from Cardiff. There is also a recording for Ireland. It is not entirely white, as the cuticle inevitably darkens a little after moulting, but long evolution underground has deprived it of eyes. Another of this genus here, less rare and less restricted to caves, is *Porrhomma convexum.* With it are the orb web spinning spider, *Meta menardi,* and the spinner of hammock web with trip wires, *Lepthyphantes pallidus.*

The cave water hog louse, *Asellus cavaticus* and the cave shrimp, *Niphargus fontanus*, are true Troglodites, as are the springtails, *Onychiurus dunarius* and *O. schoetti,* air breathing animals often found on the surface film of underground pools. Four other Collembolans here, *Schaefferia emucronata, Heteromurus nitidus, Tomocerus minor* and *Arrhopalites pygmaeus,* fall in the category of cave-lovers or Troglophiles, which are not

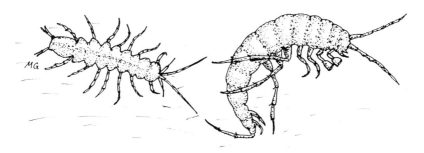

105　Two cave invertebrates: Water hog louse, *Proasellus cavaticus* and Cave shrimp, *Niphargus fontana*.

so specifically committed to life in caves. In Ogof-y-Ci these probably spend their entire lives underground, but others of their species are able to live on the surface (where they tend to seek out dark corners). This applies equally to the beetles, *Lesteva pubescens* and *Ochtephilus aureus,* the millipede, *Blaniulus guttulatus,* the woodlouse, *Androniscus dentiger* and the flatworm, *Phagocata vitta.*

The other 28 species recorded in Ogof-y-Ci belong to a third group of animals, the Trogloxenes, which spend only part of their lives in caves, often washed into them by floods, and which need to come into open stretches to breed. One such is the white trout, similar populations of which occur in cave systems of the Upper Neath and Upper Swansea Valleys and the limestone karst country of Northern England. While in the cave their pigment spots are contracted, so that they appear pale, but these expand when they swim out into the light to become normal brown trout again. Their supposed sight-lessness is a myth. Many of the food animals which they consume during their subterranean sojourn will be Trogloxenes like themselves.

Ogof-Rhyd-Sych, the lower cave, is a roosting place for lesser horseshoe bats. Jefferson found 25 animal species here, the cave water hog louse, cave shrimp, 2 Collembolans and possibly the fly, *Speolepta leptogaster,* being the only true Troglodites. An Ostracod, *Candona lucens*, a Collembolan, *Anurida granaria* and a mite, *Eugamasus loricatus,* belong to the middle group of Troglophiles.

The biological luminescence on parts of the fluted, iron-tinted calcite curtains draping the cave walls, is probably caused by Streptomycetous bacteria, but may be "moon milk", a micro-crystalline form of calcite deposited under the catalysing influence of other micro-organisms.

The Glais ashwood is confined to the narrow gorge, broadening only where it meets the splendid beech hanger at Aberglais, but its flora and fauna are rich out of all proportion to its size. There are considerable stands of snakeroot *(Polygonum bistorta)* with pink flowers and meadow saxifrage with pink bulbils in the axils of the basal leaves. Marsh valerian and marsh marigold grow in wet puddled clay below; ivy-leaved bellflower among sweet woodruff and wood sanicle in drier soil above. Herb Paris *(Paris quadrifolia)* and Welsh poppy *(Meconopsis cambrica)* are rare. Orchids which it is possible to find – but seldom all in the same season – include broad leafed helleborine, lesser butterfly, bird's nest and fragrant orchids.

Liverworts produce a profusion of spores before the trees come into leaf in Spring, in shiny black 'drumstick' capsules on *Pellia endiviaefolia (*formerly *P. fabbroniana),* oval ones on *Lophocolea cuspidata,* conical heads on *Conocephalum conicum* and umbrella-shaped ones on *Preissia quadrata.* *Scapanea nemorea (*formerly *S. nemoralis)* bears dark gemmae or asexual reproductive bodies around the apical leaves, and lush dark fronds of the slabby lichen, *Peltigera praetextata,* produce lobed isidea on the older parts – these also brushing off to form new plants.

One of the more special animals is the rose leaf hopper, *Edwardsiana rosaesugans,* which is a 'first' for Britain, the only other specimens known to science living at 2,000 metres in Switzerland. Day-flying moths include brimstones, early thorns, white waves and silver ground carpets, and comma butterflies have been seen here as late as early November. Dragonflies and damselflies, little owls and cuckoos, hedgehogs and foxes all contribute to the diversity of this tiny 7½ acre nature reserve.

The Tâf Fechan Nature Reserve

The Tâf Fechan Gorge fluctuates in width from the curvaceous confines of the water-polished chasm below the arched stone bridge at Pontsarn to the undulating expanse of wooded spoil in the old Gurnos Quarry above the mighty Heads of the Valleys road bridge. It supports calcareous communities throughout this stretch, the change to acid Millstone Grit coming a little further downstream. Tributary springs come and go, possibly due to quarrying operations and blasting at Vaynor just above. One appearing in 1971 had converted the area where it surfaced into a bed of soft-rush by 1976.

Primroses crowd sunny banks in April with wild strawberry and wood violet; wood anemones the shady ones, with dog's mercury and wood sorrel. Yellow mimulus flowers in pebbly shallows in August with spike rush and fool's watercress; betony, devil's bit scabious and golden rod on well drained slopes.

Stools of tussock sedge laced with water figwort jut out into the current and deep purple flowers of wild columbine *(Aquilegia vulgaris)* are to be found. Water avens occupies the riverside ecological niche utilised by marsh cinquefoil in South Glamorgan. The 102 acres of the 1¼ mile long Local Nature Reserve contain more species than the smaller Glais reserve, but lack at least four of the rarer flowers of that delectable tributary valley.

Jennifer Rees has investigated the gut contents of some of the river's animal life to try and unravel the lower links of the food chain. Slow movers like wandering snails and river limpets scrape encrusting blue-green algae and diatoms from the rocks, helping to alleviate their slipperiness. *Agapetis* caddis larvae and the maggots of some of the Dipterons – *Thaumalea* and soldier flies or Stratomyids do likewise. Larvae of blackfly or buffalo gnats *(Simulium)* aspire to larger plant life, consuming fragments of moss, grass and herbaceous leaves, filamentous green algae, fungal threads and even small animals, scraps of whose cuticles were found in their alimentary canals.

Freshwater shrimps seemed satisfied with detritus whilst Helodid beetle larvae add fungal and algal threads to this partially pre-digested fare. Among the caddis flies *Wormaldia* feeds on diatoms, *Diplectrona felix* on fungus and detritus. Stoneflies appear to be omnivorus during their aquatic phase and gut contents of *Nemoura erratica* varied from individual to individual and included both plant and animal material. *Nemoura cambrica* contained a pot pouri of plant fragments, *Leuctra nigra* only detritus, and the guts of the fourth species, *Protonemoura meyeri,* were empty.

The open woodland of the valley sides is notable for its turkey oaks, their bumper nut crops housed in bristly acorn cups. One sawn down in 1976 (in spite of a tree preservation order to protect them) revealed 63 annual rings. This was a mast year for beech in the reserve. Well-grown downy birches are beset with witches brooms caused by the fungus *Taphrina betulina,* these starting as bristly masses of undeveloped twiglets and splaying into the familiar shaggy tufts only when the causative fungus starts to decline, by which time they are usually inhabited by mites, *Eriophyes rudis.*

Intermittent burning of the brackenny slopes on the Brecon side, coupled with the effects of grazing, prevents woodland regeneration, but extensive tree planting is planned. By 1974, a few years after the laying of the North Sea Gas Main across the valley, the course of the buried pipe was marked by a close carpet of flowering field daisies.

When quarrying ceased at Gurnos, the spoil tips of the valley floor were planted with pines, which have long since disappeared, but the fine specimens on the cliff alongside are progeny of these. Water has drained away from the big shady pool at the foot of this cliff since the coming of the Heads of the Valleys road along the top. This was a partially quarried swallow hole and served as a breeding ground for newts and frogs. The adjacent jumble of mossy boulders provides microhabitats for shelter-loving organisms.

The flowery, hawthorn-dotted sward which has succeeded the pine plant-ation attracts all the common butterflies and several less common ones – silver-washed fritillary, ringlet, painted lady, brimstone and orange-tip. Common blues, absent for some years, were back by 1974. Nectar plants include yellow pea, great hedge bedstraw, St. John's wort and centaury.

Fungi come in many forms, some of the more bizarre being black 'witch's fingers' *(Xylaria polymorpha),* white 'wood hedgehog' *(Hydnum repandum),* honeycombed edible Morels *(Morchella esculenta)* and Portly Ceps *(Boletus scaber).* Roy Perry has identified 100 mosses and 25

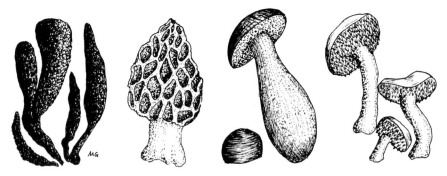

106   Four fungi: Witches's fingers, *Xylaria polymorpha*, Edible morel, *Morchella esculenta*, Portly ceps, *Boletus scaber* and *Hedgehog fungus, Hydnum repandum.*

liverworts, some, like *Neckera crispa* and *Hylocomium splendens,* uncommon in this part of South Wales.

Mosses, and liverworts may be petrified, by impregnation with lime during tufa formation. These develop best in shaded grottoes where apical growth finally fails to keep up with basal calcification. By actively extracting carbon dioxide from the bicarbonate of the spring water, the plants cause precipitation of the carbonate and hasten their own entombment. Species involved, in addition to those mentioned for the Glais, include the liverworts *Riccardia pinguis* and *P. sinuata* (with *R. glauca* further removed from the source of lime) and the mosses *Fissidens osmundoides, F. adianthoides, Gymnostomium aeruginosum* and *Trichostomum crispulum.*

Fuller accounts of the two river nature reserves have been published from time to time in bulletins of the Glamorgan Naturalists' Trust and a nature trail booklet.

The Tâf Fechan to the confluence at Cefn Coed

The change from limestone to Millstone Grit at the Heads of the Valleys road crossing is marked by a change to Rhododendron and heather on the cliffs; foxglove and lousewort on the flat. Lime-lovers like red bartsia, ploughman's spikenard, creeping cinquefoil, black medick and quaking grass, however, reappear near the lofty ruins of the lime kiln further down, with marsh arrow grass by the water. Butterbur is a feature of the river shingle, hard shield fern of the rocky valleysides, with lemon-scented mountain fern and dripping curtains of Bryophytes.

The Cyfarthfa Lake feeder canal flows more gently than the river and at a higher level. It contains curled pondweed *(Potamogeton crispus),* which occurs only in quiet backwaters of the turbulent stream below. Lesser duckweed accumulates above it, some with anomalously fused fronds and

107   Badger leaving its sett.   *Keri Williams*

extra roots in 1979. Mimulus is common to both sites, but perhaps the most remarkable water plant is the lesser reedmace *(Typha angustifolia)* in an isolated pool near the confluence. This is the more cosmopolitan of the two reedmaces on a world scale, but further south it is almost confined to a few western sites such as Oxwich Marsh, Crymlin Bog and Margam Park. Great mullein, upright hedge parsley and hemp agrimony help stabilise talus slopes held in place by entwining ash roots. The Nature Reserve ends at the A470 road bridge.

Soapwort *(Saponaria officinalis)* may have been introduced a little further upstream by the now ruined fullers' mill, its saponins a useful adjunct to wool washing. *Buddleia daviddi* established on the kiln walls tempts grayling, small copper and other butterflies, and Himalayan balsam supplies bumble and honey bees late into the autumn. Sufficient sugary fluid rises to the knapweed heads past the plundering hordes of brown aphids to furnish nectar for hover flies, drone flies, green bottles, flower flies and flower beetles.

Dippers discard piles of rifled caddis tubes on guano-whitened stones in midstream where water tumbles into two twelve foot rifts in the broad grit platform which provides such a scenic feature. Long-tailed tits forage in the alders and robins leave a litter of white fruit peels under the snowberry bushes. Starlings congregating on a pylon spatter the riverside path below

187

with scarlet debris from rowan berries and with crop pellets made from the remains of yellow ants, beetles, woodlice, seeds and fruits.

Even here, on the very brink of industrial urbanisation, yellow-fronted wagtails among drifts of monkey-flowers, and charms of goldfinches on banks of thistledown, hint of the aesthetic delights and scientific interest to be found by those who follow the two branches of the Taff into the unpredictable environment of the mountains to the north.

In the same series

THE HISTORIC TAFF VALLEY: QUAKERS YARD TO ABERFAN
by Mary Gillham, John Perkins and Clive Thomas
published September, 1979

In preparation

THE HISTORIC TAFF VALLEY: MERTHYR TYDFIL TO ABERFAN
A third volume, completing the coverage of the valley from source to the
southern boundary of the Borough of Merthyr Tydfil.